Introduction to the
LAPLACE TRANSFORM

THE APPLETON-CENTURY MATHEMATICS SERIES

Edited by Raymond W. Brink

Intermediate Algebra, 2nd ed., by Raymond W. Brink

College Algebra, 2nd ed., by Raymond W. Brink

Algebra—College Course, 2nd ed., by Raymond W. Brink

A First Year of College Mathematics, 2nd ed., by Raymond W. Brink

The Mathematics of Finance, by Franklin C. Smith

Plane Trigonometry, 3rd ed., by Raymond W. Brink

Spherical Trigonometry, by Raymond W. Brink

Essentials of Analytic Geometry, by Raymond W. Brink

Analytic Geometry, by Edwin J. Purcell

Analytic Geometry, rev. ed., by Raymond W. Brink

Analytic Geometry and Calculus, by Lloyd L. Smail

Calculus, by Lloyd L. Smail

College Geometry, by Leslie H. Miller

Solid Analytic Geometry, by John M. H. Olmsted

Intermediate Analysis, by John M. H. Olmsted

Real Variables, by John M. H. Olmsted

Introduction to the Laplace Transform, by Dio L. Holl, Clair G. Maple, and Bernard Vinograde

Introduction to the
LAPLACE TRANSFORM

by

the late Dio L. Holl

Clair G. Maple

Bernard Vinograde

IOWA STATE COLLEGE

NEW YORK: APPLETON-CENTURY-CROFTS, INC.

Preface

During the past few years it has become apparent that engineering students need a working knowledge of the Laplace transform. To fill this need a course has been developed at Iowa State College for third year students. This course has been taught 3 hours per week for a quarter from notes originally prepared by the late Professor D. L. Holl. A thorough revision of these notes based on changes contemplated by Professor Holl and suggested by teaching experience has resulted in the present text. Thus the purpose of this book is to give an introduction at the undergraduate level to the theory and applications of the Laplace transform. Although this transform is just one of the several useful transforms, it is the simplest and most commonly used, and its exposition can serve as an introduction to the general notion of an integral transform.

Our treatment is restricted to real functions in order to make it possible to teach this course at an earlier stage in the engineering curriculum. It is assumed that the student has had only the Calculus and Elementary Differential Equations. On the basis of these prerequisites, it is possible to give detailed proofs of the theorems through Chapter 3, borrowing freely well-known results from Advanced Calculus whenever necessary. In Chapters 4 and 5, we proceed almost exclusively in a formal fashion. The general plan of the book is to give the tools in the first three chapters and concentrate on applications in the next two chapters.

In Chapter 1 we assume the functions are continuous and that the necessary transforms exist. In Chapter 2 the functions are generally of exponential order and sectionally continuous. But for some common applications it is necessary to know the validity of the theorems in Chapter 2 under the less stringent conditions described in Chapter 6. Hence the necessary modifications in the proofs are given in Chapter 6.

For convenient reference a table of basic operations and a table of transforms are given in Appendixes I and II respectively. The items in these tables are cross-referenced with their initial occurrence in the text.

A glossary of terms from the Calculus is given in Appendix III. Appendix IV consists of some definitions and laws applicable to electrical circuits.

The theorems are numbered consecutively through the text in Roman numerals.

The authors wish to express their appreciation of the aid and suggestions given by Professor R. W. Brink of the University of Minnesota in the preparation of the manuscript. The authors are also indebted to their many colleagues at Iowa State College who have taught from the original notes.

C. G. M.
B. V.

Contents

++

vii

Chapter 4
Applications to Ordinary Differential Equations

Chapter 5
Applications to Linear Partial Differential Equations

Chapter 6
Transforms of Functions with Infinite Discontinuities

APPENDIXES

Introduction to the
LAPLACE TRANSFORM

1

Definition and Elementary Properties

••

1.1 INTRODUCTION

We first give the definition of the Laplace transform of a real-valued function of a real variable and develop a few of its elementary properties. Among these properties is a formula for the transform of the derivative, which together with the notion of an inverse transform enables us to use the Laplace transform technique to obtain solutions of elementary problems in ordinary differential equations.

1.2 DEFINITION OF THE LAPLACE TRANSFORM

*We define the **Laplace transform of F(t)** to be the function $f(s)$ given by*

$$(1) \qquad f(s) = \int_0^\infty e^{-st} F(t) \, dt,$$

if it exists. Here s may be any complex number, but unless otherwise indicated we will take it to be real. The function $F(t)$* is a real-valued function of the real variable t. The right-hand side of (1) is usually denoted by $L\{F(t)\}$. Thus (1) may be written in the form

$$(2) \qquad f(s) = L\{F(t)\}.$$

In order to acquire the fundamental techniques quickly we assume in this chapter that $F(t)$ is continuous for $t \geq 0$, unless otherwise

---

* We shall usually denote functions by such symbols as $F(t)$ or $f(s)$ (instead of F or f) in order to emphasize which variable is involved.

1

stated.   Consideration of functions with restricted types of discontinuities is left for Chapter 2.   We shall find the transforms of specific functions, and in the theorems we shall assume the existence of the necessary transforms, stated explicitly in each case.

As in the elementary calculus, the improper integral in (1) is defined by

$$(3) \qquad \lim_{b \to \infty} \int_0^b e^{-st} F(t)\, dt.$$

Let us find the Laplace transforms of several simple functions.

Example 1. $\displaystyle L\{1\} = \int_0^\infty 1 e^{-st}\, dt = \lim_{b \to \infty} \int_0^b e^{-st}\, dt$

$$= \lim_{b \to \infty} \left[-\frac{1}{s} e^{-st} \right]_0^b$$

$$= \lim_{b \to \infty} \left[-\frac{e^{-sb}}{s} + \frac{1}{s} \right] = \frac{1}{s}.$$

This transform exists and is equal to $\dfrac{1}{s}$ as long as s is any complex number whose real part is positive.   In particular, if s is real, then

$$(4) \qquad\qquad L\{1\} = \frac{1}{s}, \qquad (s > 0).$$

Example 2. $\displaystyle L\{t\} = \int_0^\infty t e^{-st}\, dt = \lim_{b \to \infty} \int_0^b t e^{-st}\, dt$

$$= \lim_{b \to \infty} \left[\frac{t e^{-st}}{-s} \bigg|_0^b + \frac{1}{s} \int_0^b e^{-st}\, dt \right]$$

$$= \lim_{b \to \infty} \left[\frac{b e^{-sb}}{-s} - \frac{e^{-bs}}{s^2} + \frac{1}{s^2} \right]$$

$$= \frac{1}{s^2}, \qquad (s > 0).$$

Note that the limit of the first term in the last bracket can be evaluated by use of L'Hospital's rule for indeterminate forms.

Example 3.

$$L\{t^\alpha\} = \int_0^\infty t^\alpha e^{-st}\, dt = \frac{1}{s^{\alpha+1}} \int_0^\infty x^\alpha e^{-x}\, dx, \quad (\alpha > -1, \quad s > 0).$$

In this example $F(t) = t^\alpha$ may be discontinuous at $t = 0$; yet, as we shall see, it still possesses a transform. The last integral is obtained from the preceding one by a change of the variable of integration t to $x = st$. Here we restrict s to be a real positive number and α a real number greater than -1. The improper integral $\int_0^\infty x^\alpha e^{-x}\, dx$, which exists for $\alpha > -1$, is denoted by $\Gamma(\alpha + 1)$ and is called the *gamma function* of $\alpha + 1$. Thus, we have

$$(5) \qquad L\{t^\alpha\} = \frac{\Gamma(\alpha + 1)}{s^{\alpha+1}}, \qquad (s > 0, \quad \alpha > -1).$$

We derive directly, for the particular value $\alpha = -\frac{1}{2}$, a result implied by (5):

$$(5') \qquad L\{t^{-1/2}\} = \int_0^\infty t^{-1/2} e^{-st}\, dt = \sqrt{\frac{\pi}{s}}, \qquad (s > 0).$$

Note that the integrand becomes infinite as t goes to zero, so this integral is improper at both limits. Now change the variable of integration from t to $x = \sqrt{st}$. Then

$$\int_0^\infty t^{-1/2} e^{-st}\, dt = \int_0^\infty \frac{\sqrt{s}}{x} e^{-x^2} \frac{2x\, dx}{s}$$

$$= \frac{2}{\sqrt{s}} \int_0^\infty e^{-x^2}\, dx$$

$$= \sqrt{\frac{\pi}{s}}, \qquad (s > 0).$$

We have used the fact that $\int_0^\infty e^{-x^2}\, dx = \frac{\sqrt{\pi}}{2}$, a result usually established in advanced calculus.* For positive integral values of α,

* See D. V. Widder, *Advanced Calculus* (Englewood Cliffs, N.J., Prentice-Hall, 1947), pp. 306–307.

$\Gamma(\alpha + 1) = \alpha! = 1 \cdot 2 \cdot 3 \cdots \alpha$, and for $\alpha = 0$, $\Gamma(1) = 1$, so equation (5) contains the results of Examples 1 and 2 as special cases.

From the definition of the Laplace transform it follows that it is *linear*; that is, if a and b are constants then

$$(6) \qquad L\{aF(t) + bG(t)\} = aL\{F(t)\} + bL\{G(t)\},$$

provided that any two of the three transforms needed in (6) exist. We first note that this property of the transform tells us that

$$(7) \qquad L\{cF(t)\} = cL\{F(t)\},$$

where c is any constant. In particular

$$(8) \qquad L\{c\} = cL\{1\} = \frac{c}{s}, \qquad (s > 0).$$

Furthermore, the transform of the sum of a finite number of functions is the sum of the transforms of the individual functions, provided they exist.

As an illustration of these properties, let us find the transform of a polynomial of degree n.

Example 4. $L\left\{ \sum_{i=0}^{n} a_i t^i \right\} = L\{a_0 + a_1 t + a_2 t^2 + \cdots + a_n t^n\}$

$$= \sum_{i=0}^{n} a_i L\{t^i\} = a_0 L\{1\} + a_1 L\{t\} + a_2 L\{t^2\} + \cdots + a_n L\{t^n\}$$

$$= \sum_{i=0}^{n} a_i \frac{\Gamma(i+1)}{s^{i+1}} = \frac{a_0}{s} + \frac{a_1}{s^2} + \frac{2! a_2}{s^3} + \cdots + \frac{n! a_n}{s^{n+1}}, \qquad (s > 0).$$

Here we have introduced the conventional summation symbol $\sum_{i=0}^{n}$. More generally, $\sum_{i=p}^{q} u_i = u_p + u_{p+1} + \cdots + u_q, (p \leq q$, both integers), where the left-hand side of this equality is an abbreviated form for the right-hand side.

Example 5. $L\{\cos kt\} = \displaystyle\int_0^\infty e^{-st} \cos kt \, dt, \; (s > 0).$ Repeated application of integration by parts gives

$$L\{\cos kt\} = \frac{e^{-st}\cos kt}{-s}\Bigg]_0^\infty - \frac{k}{s}\int_0^\infty e^{-st}\sin kt\, dt$$

$$= \frac{1}{s} - \frac{k}{s}\left[\frac{e^{-st}}{-s}\sin kt\,\Bigg|_0^\infty + \frac{k}{s}\int_0^\infty e^{-st}\cos kt\, dt\right]$$

$$= \frac{1}{s} - \frac{k^2}{s^2}\int_0^\infty e^{-st}\cos kt\, dt$$

$$= \frac{1}{s} - \frac{k^2}{s^2}L\{\cos kt\}.$$

If we solve for $L\{\cos kt\}$, we get

(9) $$L\{\cos kt\} = \frac{s}{s^2 + k^2}, \qquad (s > 0).$$

Example 6. $$L\{e^{\beta t}\} = \int_0^\infty e^{\beta t}e^{-st}\, dt = \int_0^\infty e^{-(s-\beta)t}\, dt$$

$$= \frac{e^{-(s-\beta)t}}{-(s-\beta)}\Bigg]_0^\infty = \frac{1}{s-\beta}.$$

This result is obtained on the assumption that $s > \beta$. Thus we have

(10) $$L\{e^{\beta t}\} = \frac{1}{s-\beta}, \qquad (s > \beta).$$

We note that the above is still valid for complex values of s and β for which $R(s) > R(\beta)$. ($R(s)$ means the real part of s.)

If we use equation (10) and the linearity property of the Laplace transform as given by (6), we can compute the transforms of hyperbolic functions with very little additional effort. To illustrate this, we first recall the definition of the hyperbolic sine of x and then find its Laplace transform. By definition, $\sinh x = \dfrac{e^x - e^{-x}}{2}$. Hence

$$L\{\sinh kt\} = L\left\{\frac{e^{kt} - e^{-kt}}{2}\right\} = \tfrac{1}{2}[L\{e^{kt}\} - L\{e^{-kt}\}].$$

Now by (10), this becomes

$$L\{\sinh kt\} = \frac{1}{2}\left[\frac{1}{s-k} - \frac{1}{s+k}\right],$$

thus

(11) $$L\{\sinh kt\} = \frac{k}{s^2 - k^2}, \qquad (s > |k|).$$

EXERCISES I

1. Find the following transforms:

   (a) $L\{3 + 2t\}$.   (d) $L\{5 \sinh 3t\}$.

   (b) $L\{t^2\}$.   (e) $L\{1 - \cos 2t\}$.

   (c) $L\{6e^{-2t}\}$.

2. (a) Use repeated integration by parts to show that if $P(t)$ is a polynomial then, apart from an additive constant,

$$\int e^{at} P(t)\, dt = \frac{1}{a} e^{at} \left[P(t) - \frac{1}{a} P'(t) + \frac{1}{a^2} P''(t) - \cdots \right].$$

   (b) Apply the above formula to find

$$L\{5 - t + 2t^2 + t^3\}.$$

3. Ignore the limits in Example 5 to show that

$$\int e^{-st} \cos kt\, dt = \frac{e^{-st}(k \sin kt - s \cos kt)}{s^2 + k^2},$$

apart from an additive arbitrary constant.

4. Use integration by parts to show that

$$\int e^{-st} \sin kt\, dt = \frac{-e^{-st}(s \sin kt + k \cos kt)}{s^2 + k^2},$$

apart from an additive constant.   Then use this result to show that

$$L\{\sin kt\} = \frac{k}{s^2 + k^2}, \qquad (s > 0).$$

5. Given that the hyperbolic cosine of kt is defined by

$$\cosh kt = \frac{e^{kt} + e^{-kt}}{2},$$

show that

$$L\{\cosh kt\} = \frac{s}{s^2 - k^2}, \qquad (s > |k|).$$

6. (a) Given that

$$\cos kt + i \sin kt = e^{ikt},$$

where $i^2 = -1$, and assuming that equation (6) is valid for complex values of a and b, use the results of 3 and 4 above to show that

$$L\{e^{ikt}\} = L\{\cos kt + i \sin kt\} = \frac{s}{s^2 + k^2} + i\frac{k}{s^2 + k^2}$$

$$= \frac{1}{s - ik}, \qquad (s > 0).$$

Observe that this result may be obtained formally by setting $\beta = ik$ in equation (10).

(b) Extend the results of part (a) above as follows: First show that (10) implies formally that

$$L\{e^{(a+ik)t}\} = \frac{1}{s - (a + ik)}.$$

Then use the formula $e^{ikt} = \cos kt + i \sin kt$ to show that

$$L\{e^{at} \cos kt\} = \frac{s - a}{(s - a)^2 + k^2}, \qquad (s > a),$$

$$L\{e^{at} \sin kt\} = \frac{k}{(s - a)^2 + k^2}, \qquad (s > a).$$

(c) Apply the results of part (b) above to find:

  i. $L\{3e^{-t} \sin 2t\}$.

  ii. $L\{4e^{2t} \cos 3t\}$.

7. Use the equations (5) and (5′) to show that

$$\Gamma(1/2) = \sqrt{\pi}.$$

1.3 TRANSLATION AND SCALE CHANGE OF THE TRANSFORM

It is convenient for future work to have rapid methods for acquiring transforms. The following two theorems are directed toward that end.

Theorem I. *Translation Theorem.* *If* $f(s) = L\{F(t)\}$ *exists for* $s \geq s_0$, *then for any constant* a,

(1) $$L\{e^{at}F(t)\} = f(s-a), \qquad (s \geq s_0 + a).$$

Proof. By definition

$$f(s) = \int_0^\infty e^{-st}F(t)\,dt.$$

Now if $f(s)$ is "translated" by replacing s by $s - a$, we get

$$f(s-a) = \int_0^\infty e^{-(s-a)t}F(t)\,dt = \int_0^\infty e^{-st}(e^{at}F(t))\,dt = L\{e^{at}F(t)\}.$$

Theorem II. *Change of Scale.* *If* $f(s) = L\{F(t)\}$ *exists for* $s \geq s_0$, *then*

(2) $$L\{F(at)\} = \frac{1}{a}f\left(\frac{s}{a}\right), \qquad (a > 0, s \geq as_0).$$

Proof. If in the definition of $f(s)$, we replace s by $\dfrac{s}{a}$ we get

$$f\left(\frac{s}{a}\right) = \int_0^\infty e^{-s\frac{t}{a}}F(t)\,dt.$$

If we now change the variable of integration by setting $t = ax$, we have

$$f\left(\frac{s}{a}\right) = \int_0^\infty e^{-sx}F(ax)a\,dx = aL\{F(at)\}.$$

1.4 THE INVERSE TRANSFORM

In §1.2 we introduced the notation

$$f(s) = L\{F(t)\}$$

to denote the transform of a known function $F(t)$. There we were concerned with finding the transform $f(s)$. Now suppose we consider the inverse problem. Given a function of s, say $f(s)$, find a function $F(t)$ whose transform is $f(s)$. To facilitate our discussion of the new problem we introduce the notation

(1) $$F(t) = L^{-1}\{f(s)\}.$$

In words, $F(t)$ equals the *inverse transform* of $f(s)$. This brings up the question of the uniqueness of $F(t)$ in equation (1) when $f(s)$ is given.   For the purposes of this chapter we need the following fact, which we give without proof:*   If $F(t)$ and $G(t)$ are continuous for $t \geq 0$, and if $L\{F(t)\} = L\{G(t)\} = f(s)$ for $s \geq s_0$, then $F(t) \equiv G(t)$ for $t \geq 0$.   This fact justifies the use of Laplace transform tables (such as given in Appendix II) for finding inverse transforms.   Thus in Example 5, §1.2, we showed that the transform of $\cos kt$ is equal

to $\dfrac{s}{s^2 + k^2}$.   However, up to this point we have had no assurance that this is the only continuous function of t whose transform is

$\dfrac{s}{s^2 + k^2}$.   The theorem just quoted lets us make the statement that

$$L^{-1}\left\{\frac{s}{s^2 + k^2}\right\} = \cos kt$$

is the only continuous inverse transform of $\dfrac{s}{s^2 + k^2}$.

More generally we may use any formula for the transform of a continuous function as a formula for the continuous inverse transform.   In particular, formulas (1) and (2) of Theorems I and II may be written

$$(2) \qquad L^{-1}\{f(s - a)\} = e^{at}F(t), \qquad (s \geq s_0 + a),$$

$$(3) \qquad L^{-1}\left\{f\left(\frac{s}{a}\right)\right\} = aF(at), \qquad (a > 0, s \geq as_0).$$

From (6), §1.2, we have further,

$$(4) \qquad L^{-1}\{af(s) + bg(s)\} = aL^{-1}\{f(s)\} + bL^{-1}\{g(s)\},$$

where $f(s) = L\{F(t)\}$ and $g(s) = L\{G(t)\}$.

EXERCISES 2

1.   Find (a) $L\{te^{3t}\}$.

(b) $L\{(1 - t)e^{-t}\}$.

(c) $L\{t^3e^{5t}\}$.

* See D. V. Widder, *Advanced Calculus* (Englewood Cliffs, N.J., Prentice-Hall, 1947), pp. 386–387.

2. Show that

(5) $\quad L\{e^{at}t^n\} = \dfrac{n!}{(s-a)^{n+1}}, \qquad (s > a, \ n \text{ positive and integral}).$

Note that this formula can be extended by application of equation (5), §1.2, to read

$$L\{e^{at}t^n\} = \frac{\Gamma(n+1)}{(s-a)^{n+1}}, \qquad (s > a, \ n > -1).$$

3. (a) If $f(s) = L\{F(t)\}$, show that $L\{\cosh t \cdot F(t)\} = \frac{1}{2}[f(s-1) + f(s+1)]$, using the exponential definition of $\cosh t$. Apply this result to show that

$$L\{t^n \cosh at\} = \frac{n!}{2}\left[\frac{1}{(s-a)^{n+1}} + \frac{1}{(s+a)^{n+1}}\right],$$

for n positive and integral, $s > |a|$.

(b) Use the same method to show that

$$L\{t^n \sinh at\} = \frac{n!}{2}\left[\frac{1}{(s-a)^{n+1}} - \frac{1}{(s+a)^{n+1}}\right].$$

4. Show that

(a) $L\{\cosh^2 t\} = \dfrac{s^2 - 2}{s(s^2 - 4)}, \qquad (s > 2).$

(b) $L\{\sinh^2 t\} = \dfrac{2}{s(s^2 - 4)}, \qquad (s > 2).$

5. Use Theorem II and the fact that $L\{\sin t\} = \dfrac{1}{s^2 + 1}$ to prove that $L\{\sin kt\} = \dfrac{k}{s^2 + k^2}$.

6. Find (a) $L^{-1}\left\{\dfrac{6}{(s+1)^2 + 4}\right\}.$ (b) $L^{-1}\left\{\dfrac{2}{(s+3)}\right\}.$

(c) $L^{-1}\left\{\dfrac{8s + 16}{(s+2)^2 - 9}\right\}.$ (d) $L^{-1}\left\{\dfrac{1}{81s^2 + 16}\right\}.$

1.5 TRANSFORMS OF DERIVATIVES

One of the principal applications of Laplace transforms is to get solutions of differential equations. For this application we must be able to express the transform of the derivative of a function in terms of the transform of the function. Such a relation is given by the following theorem.

Theorem III. *Derivative Theorem. Let $F(t)$ and $F'(t)$ be continuous for $t \geq 0$, and assume the existence of $L\{F(t)\}$ and $L\{F'(t)\}$ for $s \geq s_0$. Then*

(1) $$L\{F'(t)\} = sL\{F(t)\} - F(0), \qquad (s > s_0).$$

Proof. By definition,

$$L\{F'(t) = \lim_{b \to \infty} \int_0^b F'(t)e^{-st}\,dt.$$

Integrating by parts, we get

$$\int_0^b e^{-st}F'(t)\,dt = e^{-st}F(t)\Big|_0^b + s\int_0^b e^{-st}F(t)\,dt.$$

Hence

(2) $$\int_0^b e^{-st}F'(t)\,dt = s\int_0^b e^{-st}F(t)\,dt - F(0) + e^{-sb}F(b).$$

Now, the theorem will be proved if we show that

$$\lim_{b \to \infty} e^{-sb}F(b) = 0.$$

Since the limits of all terms in (2), except for $e^{-sb}F(b)$, are assumed to exist, we infer the existence of some number M_0 such that

$$\lim_{b \to \infty} e^{-s_0 b}F(b) = M_0.$$

Suppose $s = s_0 + \sigma$ where $\sigma > 0$. Then

(3) $$\lim_{b \to \infty} e^{-sb}F(b) = \left[\lim_{b \to \infty} e^{-s_0 b}F(b)\right]\left[\lim_{b \to \infty} e^{-\sigma b}\right] = M_0 \cdot 0 = 0.$$

Now letting b approach infinity in (2), we get

$$L\{F'(t)\} = sL\{F(t)\} - F(0), \qquad (s > s_0).$$

Example. The above theorem may be used to find transforms indirectly. To illustrate this method, let us again find $L\{te^{at}\}$.

If we set $F(t) = te^{at}$, then $F'(t) = ate^{at} + e^{at}$. Substitution of $F'(t)$ into (1) gives

$$L\{ate^{at} + e^{at}\} = sL\{te^{at}\} - F(0),$$

or

$$aL\{te^{at}\} + \frac{1}{s-a} = sL\{te^{at}\}, \qquad (s > a),$$

since $F(0) = 0$. Hence

$$(4) \qquad L\{te^{at}\} = \frac{1}{(s-a)^2}, \qquad (s > a).$$

We may then use this result to get $L\{t^2e^{at}\}$. For, if we set

$$G(t) = tF(t) = t^2e^{at},$$

then

$$G'(t) = tF'(t) + F(t).$$

Hence

$$L\{G'(t)\} = L\{tF'(t) + F(t)\} = sL\{G(t)\} - G(0),$$

or

$$L\{tF'(t)\} + f(s) = sg(s).$$

That is,

$$L\{at^2e^{at} + te^{at}\} + f(s) = sg(s),$$

or

$$ag(s) + 2f(s) = sg(s),$$

hence

$$(5) \qquad g(s) = \frac{2}{(s-a)^3}, \qquad (s > a).$$

In applications of the Laplace transform to ordinary differential equations it is necessary to find transforms of second and higher order derivatives, when these transforms exist. The second derivative is the most important for us, hence we extend Theorem III as follows:

Corollary. *If $F'(t)$ and $F''(t)$ are continuous for $t \geq 0$, and if $L\{F(t)\}, L\{F'(t)\}$, and $L\{F''(t)\}$ exist for $s \geq s_0$, then*

$$(6) \qquad L\{F''(t)\} = s^2f(s) - sF(0) - F'(0), \qquad (s > s_0).$$

Proof. By Theorem III, formula (1), we may transform $F''(t)$ as follows:

$$L\{F''(t)\} = sL\{F'(t)\} - F'(0), \qquad (s > s_0).$$

Since the continuity of $F'(t)$ implies the continuity of $F(t)$, we may apply (1) to $F'(t)$ to get

$$L\{F'(t)\} = sf(s) - F(0), \qquad (s > s_0).$$

Hence $L\{F''(t)\} = s[sf(s) - F(0)] - F'(0)$

$$= s^2 f(s) - sF(0) - F'(0).$$

We note without proof the following extension of this corollary: If $F(t)$ and its first n derivatives are continuous for $t \geq 0$, and if $L\{F(t)\}, L\{F'(t)\}, \cdots, L\{F^{(n)}(t)\}$, exist for $s \geq s_0$, then

(7) $\quad L\{F^{(n)}(t)\} = s^n f(s) - s^{n-1}F(0) - s^{n-2}F'(0) - \cdots - F^{(n-1)}(0),$

$$(s > s_0).$$

EXERCISES 3

1. Use Theorem III to show that:

(a) Since $L\{1\} = \dfrac{1}{s}$, hence $L\{t\} = \dfrac{1}{s^2}$.

(b) Since $L\{\sin kt\} = \dfrac{k}{s^2 + k^2}$, hence $L\{\cos kt\} = \dfrac{s}{s^2 + k^2}$.

2. Given $L\{\sin kt\} = \dfrac{k}{s^2 + k^2}$ and $L\{\cos kt\} = \dfrac{s}{s^2 + k^2}$, use the corollary to show that:

(a) $L\{t \sin kt\} = \dfrac{2ks}{(s^2 + k^2)^2}$.

(b) $L\{t \cos kt\} = \dfrac{s^2 - k^2}{(s^2 + k^2)^2}$.

3. Use the corollary to show that:

(a) $L\{t \sinh kt\} = \dfrac{2ks}{(s^2 - k^2)^2}$.

(b) $L\{t \cosh kt\} = \dfrac{s^2 + k^2}{(s^2 - k^2)^2}$.

4. If $L\{F(t)\} = f(s)$, show that:

$$L\{4F''(t) - 4F'(t) + F(t)\} = (2s - 1)^2 f(s) - 4(s - 2),$$

provided $F(0) = 1$ and $F'(0) = -1$.

1.6 DIFFERENTIAL EQUATIONS

The Laplace transform gives us a method that is especially suitable for the solution of ordinary linear differential equations with constant coefficients, particularly when we seek that solution which satisfies boundary conditions on the unknown function and its derivatives

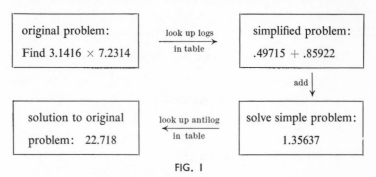

FIG. I

all of which are specified at a single point.   Under the assumption that the necessary transforms exist, the Laplace transform method consists of three basic steps:

(*a*) Take the Laplace transform of each side of the given differential equation and equate to obtain an algebraic equation in the transform of the unknown function.

(*b*) Solve the algebraic equation obtained in step (*a*) for the transform of the unknown function.

(*c*) Find the inverse transform.

The method described above is quite analogous to the method of logarithms in multiplication or extraction of roots of real numbers. For example, the problem of finding the product of two numbers A and B is reduced to a simple problem of addition when logarithms are used.   To be specific, we find the product 3.1416×7.2314 by use of logarithms and illustrate the procedure in the diagram given in Fig. 1.

To illustrate the Laplace transform method of solving a differential system (a differential equation and the associated boundary conditions) and at the same time its analogy to the use of logarithms, we give the following example.

Example 1.   Find the solution of the equation

$$\frac{dX}{dt} + 2X = e^{-2t},$$

which satisfies the initial condition $X(0) = 1$.

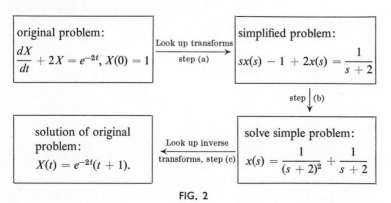

FIG. 2

If we take the transform of both sides of this equation (step (a)), making use of Theorem III, §1.5 and the initial condition, we get

$$sx(s) - 1 + 2x(s) = \frac{1}{s+2}, \qquad \text{where } x(s) = L\{X(t)\}.$$

Solving for $x(s)$, (step (b)), we get

$$x(s) = \frac{1}{(s+2)^2} + \frac{1}{s+2}.$$

Therefore by step (c), we have

$$X(t) = L^{-1}\left\{\frac{1}{(s+2)^2}\right\} + L^{-1}\left\{\frac{1}{s+2}\right\} = te^{-2t} + e^{-2t} = e^{-2t}(t+1).$$

These steps are illustrated in the diagram given in Fig. 2. This should be compared to the diagram given in Fig. 1.

The solution which we obtained formally in Example 1 checks, and is in fact the only solution. More generally, for any equation of the form

$$\frac{dX}{dt} + a(t)X = R(t)$$

with the boundary condition $X(0) = C$, where $a(t)$ and $R(t)$ are continuous and C is a constant, it follows from the elementary theory of ordinary differential equations that there exists a unique solution* possessing a continuous first derivative.

The corollary of §1.5 and the remarks following it enable us to extend the method for first order differential equations given above to differential equations of higher order. In particular the Laplace transform method is especially convenient for getting solutions of linear differential equations of the form

$$\frac{d^n X}{dt^n} + a_1(t)\frac{d^{n-1}X}{dt^{n-1}} + \cdots + a_{n-1}(t)\frac{dX}{dt} + a_n(t)X = R(t),$$

with boundary conditions

$$X^{(k)}(0) = C_k, \qquad (k = 0, 1, 2, \cdots, n-1),$$

where $X^{(k)}(t)$ is the kth order derivative of $X(t)$ and $X^{(0)}(t)$ is $X(t)$. When the solution function and its derivatives are specified for $t = 0$, the assumption that the coefficients $a_k(t)$, $(k = 1, 2, \cdots, n)$ and the right-hand side $R(t)$ are continuous assures us that there exists a unique solution* with continuous derivatives up to and including the nth order. Hence when the result of a formal application of transforms has these properties and checks, it is the desired solution.

We illustrate the Laplace transform method for higher order differential equations by finding the solution of a second order differential system with constant coefficients.

Example 2. Find the solution of the differential equation

$$X''(t) - 4X'(t) + 4X(t) = 0$$

which satisfies the boundary conditions

$$X(0) = 0, \qquad X'(0) = 1.$$

---

* R. P. Agnew, *Differential Equations* (New York, McGraw-Hill, 1942), p. 317.

By the corollary of §1.5 the transform of the given equation is

$$s^2x(s) - sX(0) - X'(0) - 4[sx(s) - X(0)] + 4x(s) = 0.$$

The boundary conditions permit us to reduce this to the form

$$(s^2 - 4s + 4)x(s) = 1,$$

or

$$x(s) = \frac{1}{(s-2)^2}.$$

Hence, finding the inverse transform, we have the desired solution given by

$$X(t) = L^{-1}\{x(s)\} = te^{2t}.$$

If the boundary condition on the solution function and the condition on its derivative are given for different values of t, the transform method is still applicable with slight variation as illustrated in the following example.

Example 3. Find the solution of the equation

$$X''(t) + 4X(t) = 0$$

which satisfies the conditions $X(0) = 1$, $X\left(\dfrac{\pi}{4}\right) = -1$.

The transformed equation is

$$s^2x(s) - sX(0) - X'(0) + 4x(s) = 0.$$

Now $X(0) = 1$, but the value of $X'(0)$ is not known, so we carry it along as an arbitrary constant which will be determined later.   Thus, solving for $x(s)$, we get

$$x(s) = \frac{s}{s^2+4} + X'(0)\,\frac{1}{s^2+4}$$

$$= \frac{s}{s^2+4} + \frac{X'(0)}{2}\cdot\frac{2}{s^2+4}.$$

Hence

$$X(t) = \cos 2t + \frac{X'(0)}{2}\sin 2t.$$

Setting $t = \dfrac{\pi}{4}$ and using the condition $X\left(\dfrac{\pi}{4}\right) = -1$ we get

$$-1 = 0 + \frac{X'(0)}{2} \cdot 1.$$

Thus $X'(0) = -2$ and therefore the solution we seek is

$$X(t) = \cos 2t - \sin 2t.$$

The method of partial fractions, which the student has encountered in elementary algebra and the calculus and which will be treated in more detail in the next section, can be applied to evaluate $L^{-1}\{x(s)\}$ when $x(s)$ is a quotient of polynomials. The following example illustrates this in a simple case.

Example 4. Suppose we are given the differential system

$$X'(t) + X(t) = e^{2t}, \qquad X(0) = 0.$$

Taking transforms, we obtain

$$sx(s) + x(s) = \frac{1}{s - 2}, \qquad (s > 2),$$

or

$$x(s) = \frac{1}{(s + 1)(s - 2)}.$$

We split $x(s)$ into partial fractions, that is, we determine constants A and B such that

$$\frac{1}{(s + 1)(s - 2)} = \frac{A}{s + 1} + \frac{B}{s - 2},$$

for all $s \neq 2$, $s \neq -1$. This is equivalent to requiring that

$$1 \equiv A(s - 2) + B(s + 1)$$

identically in s. Hence to determine the constants, we may equate coefficients of like powers of s,

$$A + B = 0,$$

$$-2A + B = 1,$$

which gives

$$A = -\tfrac{1}{3}, \qquad B = \tfrac{1}{3}.$$

Therefore $x(s)$ may be written in the form

$$x(s) = \frac{-1}{3}\left(\frac{1}{s+1}\right) + \frac{1}{3}\left(\frac{1}{s-2}\right),$$

whose inverse transform is the solution

$$X(t) = -\tfrac{1}{3}e^{-t} + \tfrac{1}{3}e^{2t}.$$

The method illustrated in the preceding examples may readily be extended to a system of differential equations. Here again we would like to be assured that there are solution functions; that is, that we are looking for something which does exist. Again the theory of ordinary differential equations provides an existence theorem which tells us that under rather general conditions we can be assured of unique continuous solutions. Formal application of the Laplace transform technique gives us a method for finding the solution functions.

Example 5. Find the functions $X(t)$ and $Y(t)$ which satisfy the differential equations

$$X'(t) + Y'(t) - 4Y(t) = 1,$$

$$X(t) + Y'(t) - 3Y(t) = t^2,$$

and the initial conditions

$$X(0) = Y(0) = 0.$$

Let $x(s)$ and $y(s)$ be the transforms of $X(t)$ and $Y(t)$, respectively. Then these transforms must satisfy the system of algebraic equations

$$sx(s) + sy(s) - 4y(s) = \frac{1}{s},$$

$$x(s) + sy(s) - 3y(s) = \frac{2}{s^3}.$$

These equations may be written in the form

$$sx(s) + (s-4)y(s) = \frac{1}{s},$$

$$x(s) + (s-3)y(s) = \frac{2}{s^3}.$$

If we solve the second equation for $x(s)$ and substitute the result in the first equation we get

$$s\left[\frac{2}{s^3} - (s-3)y(s)\right] + (s-4)y(s) = \frac{1}{s},$$

or

$$(s^2 - 4s + 4)y(s) = \frac{2}{s^2} - \frac{1}{s}.$$

Hence $y(s) = \dfrac{2}{s^2(s-2)^2} - \dfrac{1}{s(s-2)^2} = \dfrac{-1}{s^2(s-2)} .$

Using the method of partial fractions, we write

$$\frac{-1}{s^2(s-2)} = \frac{A}{s} + \frac{B}{s^2} + \frac{C}{s-2},$$

or

$$-1 = (As + B)(s-2) + Cs^2.$$

Putting $s = 2$ we get $C = -\frac{1}{4}$.   For $s = 0$ we get $B = \frac{1}{2}$.   Another value of s, say $s = 1$, gives $-1 = -(A+B) + C$ and therefore $A = \frac{1}{4}$.   Hence

$$y(s) = \frac{1}{4}\left[\frac{1}{s} + \frac{2}{s^2} - \frac{1}{s-2}\right],$$

whose inverse transform is

$$Y(t) = \tfrac{1}{4}[1 + 2t - e^{2t}].$$

Having found $Y(t)$, we may substitute directly into the second of the given differential equations to find that

$$X(t) = \tfrac{1}{4}[1 + 6t + 4t^2 - e^{2t}]$$

in this particular example.   However, this last step is not always possible, in which case it is necessary to solve the system of algebraic equations in $x(s)$ and $y(s)$ for $x(s)$ and take the inverse transform to find $X(t)$.

EXERCISES 4

Find the Laplace transforms of the solutions of the following differential systems.   Solve completely for the solutions in 1, 3, and 8.

1. $X'(t) + X(t) = 1$, $X(0) = 0$.

2. $X'(t) + X(t) = \sin t$, $X(0) = 0$.

3. $X'(t) + X(t) = te^{-t}$, $X(0) = 0$.

4. $X''(t) + X(t) = e^{-t}$, $X(0) = 0$, $X'(0) = 0$.

5. $X''(t) + 4X'(t) + 4X(t) = e^{-t}$, $X(0) = 0$, $X'(0) = 0$.

6. $X''(t) - 2X'(t) = e^{t}$, $X(0) = 0$, $X'(0) = 0$.

7. $X'''(t) - 3X''(t) + 2X'(t) = 0$, $X(0) = 0$, $X'(0) = 0$,
$$X''(0) = 1.$$

8. $X''(t) + 10X'(t) + 21X(t) = 0$, $X(0) = 0$, $X(1) = e^{-3} - e^{-7}$.

9. $\begin{cases} X''(t) + X(t) + Y(t) = 0, & X(0) = 1, \quad Y(0) = -4, \\ Y''(t) - 3Y(t) - 4X(t) = 0, & X'(0) = 3, \quad Y'(0) = -10. \end{cases}$

10. $\begin{cases} Y'(t) - 3Z(t) = 5, & Y(0) = 1, \\ Y'(t) - Z'(t) - X(t) = 3 - 2t, & Z(0) = 0, \\ X'(t) + Z(t) = -1, & X(0) = 1. \end{cases}$

11. $\begin{cases} X''(t) + 4X'(t) + 2X(t) - 6Y(t) = 0, & X(0) = 1, \\ 6Y(t) - 3Z(t) = 0, & X'(0) = 0, \\ X(t) + Y(t) + Z(t) = 0. \end{cases}$

1.7 PARTIAL FRACTIONS AND THE INVERSE TRANSFORM OF THE QUOTIENT OF TWO POLYNOMIALS

If $N(s)$ and $P(s)$ are polynomials in s, with real coefficients, and if the degree of $N(s)$ is less than that of $P(s)$ then $L^{-1}\left\{\dfrac{N(s)}{P(s)}\right\}$ exists and is often easily evaluated by use of a partial fraction decomposition of $\dfrac{N(s)}{P(s)}$. We assume* the possibility of this partial fraction

* For a proof, see C. C. MacDuffee, *Theory of Equations* (New York, Wiley, 1954), p. 41. In order to introduce less familiar techniques the much used method of undetermined coefficients is not often applied in this section. As the reader will discover in the reference just cited, the division algorithm for polynomials supplies a fundamental approach to the decomposition.

decomposition in the domain of real numbers and suggest various techniques for obtaining it. In the cases we shall usually encounter, the existence of $L^{-1}\left\{\dfrac{N(s)}{P(s)}\right\}$ will be apparent from the partial fraction decomposition of $\dfrac{N(s)}{P(s)}$. We shall also consider briefly the partial fraction decomposition in the domain of complex numbers, in which $P(s)$ is factored completely into linear factors and from which the existence of $L^{-1}\left\{\dfrac{N(s)}{P(s)}\right\}$ follows in general.

It will be recalled from elementary algebra that apart from a constant factor $P(s)$ can be factored into a product of distinct real factors of two types: $(s - r)^p$ and $(s^2 + cs + d)^q$, where p and q are positive integers, and r is a real root of $P(s) = 0$. The theory of partial fraction decomposition states that $\dfrac{N(s)}{P(s)}$ is the sum of two types of sums. The first type corresponds to a factor $(s - r)^p$, and has the form

$$(1) \qquad \frac{A_1}{s - r} + \frac{A_2}{(s - r)^2} + \cdots + \frac{A_p}{(s - r)^p},$$

where $A_1, A_2, \cdots, A_p$ are constants. The second type corresponds to a factor $(s^2 + cs + d)^q$, and has the form

$$(2) \qquad \frac{C_1 s + D_1}{s^2 + cs + d} + \frac{C_2 s + D_2}{(s^2 + cs + d)^2} + \cdots + \frac{C_q s + D_q}{(s^2 + cs + d)^q},$$

where $C_1, C_2, \cdots, C_q$ and $D_1, D_2, \cdots, D_q$ are constants. It is sometimes convenient to express $s^2 + cs + d$ as $(s - a)^2 + b^2$, where $a + ib$ is an imaginary root of $P(s) = 0$. Then we may use (2) in the form

$$(2') \quad \frac{C_1(s - a) + D_1}{(s - a)^2 + b^2} + \frac{C_2(s - a) + D_2}{[(s - a)^2 + b^2]^2} + \cdots + \frac{C_q(s - a) + D_q}{[(s - a)^2 + b^2]^q}.$$

The simplest case of partial fraction decomposition occurs when all the roots of $P(s) = 0$ are real and distinct. If these roots are called $r_1, r_2, \cdots, r_n$, we must find constants $A_1, A_2, \cdots, A_n$ such that

$$(3) \qquad \frac{N(s)}{P(s)} = \frac{A_1}{s - r_1} + \frac{A_2}{s - r_2} + \cdots + \frac{A_n}{s - r_n}.$$

A quick method for the evaluation of $A_1, A_2, \cdots, A_n$ is derived as follows: Let us define $\phi_i(s)$ by

$$(4) \qquad \phi_i(s) = \left[\frac{s - r_i}{P(s)}\right] N(s), \qquad (i = 1, \cdots, n),$$

where in $(s - r_i)/P(s)$ it is understood that $s - r_i$ is cancelled from numerator and denominator. Now multiplying (3) by $s - r_i$, we obtain

$$(5) \qquad \phi_i(s) = (s - r_i)\left[\frac{A_1}{s - r_1} + \cdots + \frac{A_{i-1}}{s - r_{i-1}}\right]$$

$$+ A_i + (s - r_i)\left[\frac{A_{i+1}}{s - r_{i+1}} + \cdots + \frac{A_n}{s - r_n}\right].$$

Substituting $s = r_i$ in (5), we get

$$(6) \qquad \phi_i(r_i) = A_i, \qquad (i = 1, 2, \cdots, n).$$

Example 1. As an illustration of (3) we find the decomposition of $\dfrac{s^3 + 1}{3(s - 1)(s + 2)(s + 3)(s - 5)}$ and then use this decomposition to find the inverse transform of the given fraction.

If we set

$$\frac{s^3 + 1}{3(s - 1)(s + 2)(s + 3)(s - 5)} = \frac{A}{s - 1} + \frac{B}{s + 2} + \frac{C}{s + 3} + \frac{D}{s - 5},$$

then, by (4), we have

$$\phi_1(s) = \frac{s^3 + 1}{3(s + 2)(s + 3)(s - 5)},$$

$$\phi_2(s) = \frac{s^3 + 1}{3(s - 1)(s + 3)(s - 5)},$$

$$\phi_3(s) = \frac{s^3 + 1}{3(s - 1)(s + 2)(s - 5)},$$

$$\phi_4(s) = \frac{s^3 + 1}{3(s - 1)(s + 2)(s + 3)}.$$

Hence, by (6)

$$A = \phi_1(1) = -\frac{1}{72},$$

$$B = \phi_2(-2) = -\frac{1}{9},$$

$$C = \phi_3(-3) = \frac{13}{48},$$

$$D = \phi_4(5) = \frac{3}{16}.$$

Therefore

$$\frac{s^3 + 1}{3(s - 1)(s + 2)(s + 3)(s - 5)}$$

$$= -\frac{1}{72}\frac{1}{s - 1} - \frac{1}{9}\frac{1}{s + 2} + \frac{13}{48}\frac{1}{s + 3} + \frac{3}{16}\frac{1}{s - 5},$$

and

$$L^{-1}\left\{\frac{s^3 + 1}{3(s - 1)(s + 2)(s + 3)(s - 5)}\right\}$$

$$= -\frac{1}{72}e^t - \frac{1}{9}e^{-2t} + \frac{13}{48}e^{-3t} + \frac{3}{16}e^{5t}.$$

This method appears laborious in this description. However, it is not necessary to write out $\phi_i(s)$ since it is obtained by merely suppressing a linear factor in the denominator $P(s)$.

Example 2. Find $L^{-1}\left\{\dfrac{s^2}{(s + 1)^3}\right\}$.

Here $N(s) = s^2$ and $P(s) = (s + 1)^3$. Although $P(s)$ has but one distinct power of a linear factor, namely $(s + 1)^3$, a decomposition is possible since $N(s)$ is not constant. This decomposition may be made in several ways which we now illustrate.

(a) We can obtain it very simply by expressing s^2 as a linear combination of powers of $s + 1$, that is,

$$s^2 = (s + 1)^2 - 2(s + 1) + 1.$$

Thus,

$$\frac{s^2}{(s+1)^3} = \frac{1}{s+1} - \frac{2}{(s+1)^2} + \frac{1}{(s+1)^3},$$

and

$$L^{-1}\left\{\frac{s^2}{(s+1)^3}\right\} = e^{-t}\left[1 - 2t + \frac{t^2}{2}\right].$$

(b) We may proceed more directly although more laboriously as follows:

$$\frac{s^2}{(s+1)^3} = \frac{A}{s+1} + \frac{B}{(s+1)^2} + \frac{C}{(s+1)^3}$$

$$= \frac{A(s+1)^2 + B(s+1) + C}{(s+1)^3}.$$

The constants A, B, C will be the same as those required in order that

(7) $s^2 = A(s+1)^2 + B(s+1) + C$

hold identically in s. But this is exactly our starting point in (a) above, and the values of A, B, C are fairly obvious. In general, the approach at this point is based on the fact that two polynomials in s of degree at most n are identical when they are equal for more than n distinct values of s. Therefore in (7) we may equate coefficients of like powers of s to obtain

$$A = 1,$$
$$2A + B = 0,$$
$$A + B + C = 0,$$

which have as a solution: $A = 1$, $B = -2$, $C = 1$.

(c) We may mix our procedures by setting $s = -1$ in (7), obtaining $C = 1$. Then we may equate coefficients to obtain

$$A = 1,$$
$$A + B + 1 = 0,$$

as equations for A and B. On the other hand we may substitute any other two values for s to get two equations for A and B. In particular, if we set $s = 0$ and $s = 1$ in turn, we obtain

$$A + B + 1 = 0,$$
$$4A + 2B + 1 = 1,$$

as alternative equations for A and B.   Such an attack will show to better advantage in more difficult cases.

(d) Finally, we may systematize the use of the substitution $s = -1$ by using derivatives as follows: From (7) we get $C = 1$ as before by setting $s = -1$.   Then differentiating (7) with respect to s, we get

(8) $$2s = 2A(s + 1) + B,$$

which upon substitution of $s = -1$ yields $B = -2$.   Finally, differentiation of (8) gives

$$2 = 2A, \quad \text{or } A = 1.$$

Further illustrations of this differentiation procedure will be given in succeeding examples.

Example 3.   Let us now consider the problem of finding the inverse transform of a fraction in which the denominator is a simple mixture of an unrepeated linear factor and an unrepeated quadratic factor.   To illustrate, we treat

$$\frac{s + 1}{s(s^2 + 1)}.$$

In this case we seek constants A, B, and C such that

(9) $$\frac{s + 1}{s(s^2 + 1)} = \frac{A}{s} + \frac{Bs + C}{s^2 + 1}.$$

Multiplying (9) first by s, we get

$$\frac{s + 1}{s^2 + 1} = A + \frac{Bs^2 + Cs}{s^2 + 1}.$$

For $s = 0$, this reduces to $A = 1$.   Now multiplying (9) by $s^2 + 1$, we get

$$\frac{s + 1}{s} = \frac{A(s^2 + 1)}{s} + Bs + C.$$

For $s = i$ (that is, $s^2 + 1 = 0$), this reduces to

$$\frac{i + 1}{i} = Bi + C.$$

Hence $B = -1$ and $C = 1$. Consequently,

$$L^{-1}\left\{\frac{s+1}{s(s^2+1)}\right\} = L^{-1}\left\{\frac{1}{s}\right\} + L^{-1}\left\{\frac{-s+1}{s^2+1}\right\} = 1 - \cos t + \sin t.$$

Example 4. Consider now a fraction whose denominator has a single quadratic factor and a repeated linear factor as illustrated by

$$\frac{s+1}{s^2(s^2+s+1)}.$$

We seek constants A, B, C, and D such that

(10) $$\frac{s+1}{s^2(s^2+s+1)} = \frac{A}{s} + \frac{B}{s^2} + \frac{Cs+D}{s^2+s+1}$$

Here we are applying (1) with $r = 0$, $p = 2$, $A = A_1$, and $B = A_2$; and (2) with $c = d = 1$, $q = 1$, $C_1 = C$, and $D_1 = D$.

Sometimes a decomposition into partial fractions may be obtained quickly by special techniques. Thus in the present case, adding and subtracting s^2 to the numerator leads to the partial fraction decomposition immediately. In fact, even comparing coefficients of like powers of s is simple for this example.

We may conveniently obtain A and B independently of C and D, as may be deduced from the following computations. To compute B we multiply (10) by s^2, getting

(11) $$\frac{s+1}{s^2+s+1} = As + B + \frac{Cs^3+Ds^2}{s^2+s+1}.$$

Then setting $s = 0$, we obtain $B = 1$. To compute A, we differentiate (11) with respect to s to get

$$\frac{s^2+s+1-(s+1)(2s+1)}{(s^2+s+1)^2}$$

$$= A + \frac{(s^2+s+1)(3Cs^2+2Ds) - (Cs^3+Ds^2)(2s+1)}{(s^2+s+1)^2}$$

$$= A + [\text{a function which equals zero at } s = 0].$$

Clearly, for $s = 0$ we obtain $A = 0$.

Or, to compute C and D (independently of A and B), we multiply (10) by $s^2 + s + 1$, so that

$$\frac{s+1}{s^2} = \frac{A(s^2 + s + 1)}{s} + \frac{B(s^2 + s + 1)}{s^2} + Cs + D.$$

Setting s equal to a root of $s^2 + s + 1 = 0$ (which amounts to using $s^2 = -s - 1$), we obtain

$$Cs + D = -1.$$

But since one root of $s^2 + s + 1 = 0$ is $-\frac{1}{2} + \frac{i}{2}\sqrt{3}$, the last equation yields

$$C\left(-\frac{1}{2} + \frac{i}{2}\sqrt{3}\right) + D = -1,$$

or

$$C = 0, \qquad D = -1.$$

The preceding computations show that

$$\frac{s+1}{s^2(s^2 + s + 1)} = \frac{1}{s^2} - \frac{1}{s^2 + s + 1}.$$

The inverse transform of our given fraction may be obtained as follows:

$$L^{-1}\left\{\frac{1}{s^2} - \frac{1}{s^2 + s + 1}\right\} = L^{-1}\left\{\frac{1}{s^2}\right\} - L^{-1}\left\{\frac{2}{\sqrt{3}} \frac{\frac{\sqrt{3}}{2}}{\left(s + \frac{1}{2}\right)^2 + \left(\frac{\sqrt{3}}{2}\right)^2}\right\}$$

$$= t - \frac{2}{\sqrt{3}} e^{-\frac{1}{2}t} \sin \frac{\sqrt{3}}{2} t.$$

Example 5. The method of Example 1 can be extended to the case of distinct quadratic factors. For example, consider $\dfrac{2s}{(s^2 + 1)(s^2 + 2)}$.

By (2), we may write

$$(12) \qquad \frac{2s}{(s^2 + 1)(s^2 + 2)} = \frac{As + B}{s^2 + 1} + \frac{Cs + D}{s^2 + 2}.$$

If we multiply (12) by $s^2 + 1$, we obtain

(13) $$\frac{2s}{s^2 + 2} = As + B + (s^2 + 1)\frac{Cs + D}{s^2 + 2}.$$

Then multiplying (12) by $s^2 + 2$, we get

(14) $$\frac{2s}{s^2 + 1} = (s^2 + 2)\frac{As + B}{s^2 + 1} + Cs + D.$$

Now let us denote the left-hand sides of (13) and (14) by

$$\psi_1(s) = \frac{2s}{s^2 + 2}$$

and

$$\psi_2(s) = \frac{2s}{s^2 + 1},$$

respectively.   Then we have

$$\psi_1(i) = 2i = Ai + B,$$

$$\psi_2(i\sqrt{2}) = -2i\sqrt{2} = C(i\sqrt{2}) + D.$$

These equations may be solved for A, B, C, D by equating real and imaginary parts.   Thus, $A = 2$, $B = 0$, $C = -2$, and $D = 0$.
Hence the inverse transform of $\dfrac{2s}{(s^2 + 1)(s^2 + 2)}$ is given by

$$L^{-1}\left\{\frac{2s}{s^2 + 1} - \frac{2s}{s^2 + 2}\right\} = 2\cos t - 2\cos\sqrt{2}t.$$

As in Example 1, this procedure is much simplified in practice since $\psi_i(s)$ need not be written down.   The student should also note that this fraction can be quickly decomposed by the undetermined coefficient technique.

Example 6.   As another illustration of (2), let us consider the case of a repeated quadratic factor, for instance, $\dfrac{2s^3 + 1}{(s^2 + 4)^2}$.

By (2), we have

(15) $$\frac{2s^3 + 1}{(s^2 + 4)^2} = \frac{As + B}{s^2 + 4} + \frac{Cs + D}{(s^2 + 4)^2}.$$

We first multiply by the highest power of the repeated factor and obtain

(16) $$2s^3 + 1 = (As + B)(s^2 + 4) + Cs + D.$$

Now, substituting $s = 2i$ in (16), we obtain

$$-16i + 1 = 2Ci + D.$$

Hence, we have $D = 1$ and $C = -8$. At this point we have a choice of several procedures, of which we give three.

(a) We may differentiate (16) and substitute $s = 2i$. Thus

$$6s^2 = (As + B)(2s) + A(s^2 + 4) - 8$$

yields

$$-24 = 4i(2Ai + B) - 8,$$

from which we see that

$$A = 2 \quad \text{and} \quad B = 0.$$

(b) We may compare coefficients of like powers in (16), or first we may substitute $s = 0$ in (16) to get $B = 0$, and

$$2s^3 + 1 = As(s^2 + 4) - 8s + 1,$$

from which it is clear that $A = 2$.

(c) In (15) we may transpose the fraction $\dfrac{Cs + D}{(s^2 + 4)^2}$ to get

$$\frac{2s^3 + 1}{(s^2 + 4)^2} - \frac{-8s + 1}{(s^2 + 4)^2} = \frac{As + B}{s^2 + 4}.$$

Hence, we have

$$2s = As + B,$$

which yields $A = 2$ and $B = 0$.

If we operate in the domain of complex numbers, then we can factor $P(s)$ completely into linear factors and thus express $\dfrac{N(s)}{P(s)}$ as a sum of sums of type (1). However, the constants are now complex numbers. Thus in Example 6, we would seek complex constants A, B, C, D such that

(17) $$\frac{2s^3 + 1}{(s^2 + 4)^2} = \frac{A}{s + 2i} + \frac{B}{(s + 2i)^2} + \frac{C}{s - 2i} + \frac{D}{(s - 2i)^2}.$$

If we assume the validity of (5), §1.4 for complex s, we may write

(18) $$L^{-1}\left\{\frac{1}{(s-r)^p}\right\} = \frac{t^{p-1}e^{rt}}{(p-1)!},$$

and thus compute the inverse transform of (17).

EXERCISES 5

Use partial fraction decomposition to find the inverse transform of each of the following:

1. $\dfrac{s^2-5}{(s-1)(s-2)(s-3)}$.

2. $\dfrac{s^2+1}{s^2(s^2-1)}$.

3. $\dfrac{s+2}{(s-1)^2 s^3}$.

4. $\dfrac{k^2}{s(s^2+k^2)}$.

5. $\dfrac{2k^3}{s^4-k^4}$.

6. $\dfrac{2k^2 s}{s^4-k^4}$.

7. $\dfrac{2ks^2}{s^4-k^4}$.

8. $\dfrac{2s^3}{s^4-k^4}$.

9. $\dfrac{1}{(s+2)(s+1)^2(s^2+1)}$.

10. $\dfrac{s}{(s^2+a^2)(s^2+b^2)}$.

11. $\dfrac{3}{(s^2+9)(s^2-2s+5)}$.

12. $\dfrac{140}{(s^2+9)(s^2+4)(s^2+16)}$.

13. $\dfrac{70s^3+420s}{(s^2+9)(s^2+4)(s^2+16)}$.

14. Complete the solutions of 2, 5, 6, and 11 in Exercises 4.

15. If the polynomial $P(s)$ is of degree n and if $P(s) = 0$ has all real distinct roots $a_1, \cdots, a_n$, show that

$$L^{-1}\left\{\frac{N(s)}{P(s)}\right\} = \sum_{k=1}^{n} \phi(a_k)e^{a_k t}, \qquad \text{where } \phi(s) = \frac{s-a_k}{P(s)} N(s).$$

16. Complete the solutions of 9 and 10 in Exercises 4.

2

Transforms of Discontinuous Functions, Convolution Theorem, and Additional Properties

++

2.1 INTRODUCTION

In Chapter 1 we assumed for simplicity that $F(t)$ was continuous when $t \geq 0$. But this condition is neither necessary nor sufficient for the existence of $L\{F(t)\}$. Hence in the hypotheses of our theorems we postulated the existence of the desired transforms.

However, for any given function $F(t)$ it is desirable to be able to test for the existence of $L\{F(t)\}$. Therefore, in the following section we describe conditions which are fairly easy to check and which assure the existence of $L\{F(t)\}$. If a function $F(t)$ satisfies these conditions we shall call $F(t)$ a function of *class T*.

2.2 SUFFICIENT CONDITIONS FOR THE EXISTENCE OF $L\{F(t)\}$

A function $F(t)$ is said to be of *exponential order e^{at}* if corresponding to the constant a there exists a pair of positive constants t_0 and M such that for all t at which $F(t)$ is defined and $t > t_0$,

(1)
$$\left| e^{-at} F(t) \right| \leq M.$$

Intuitively this expresses the fact that $F(t)$ does not grow faster than Me^{at} as t tends to infinity. A consequence of (1) is

(2)
$$\lim_{t \to \infty} \left| e^{-a't} F(t) \right| = 0, \qquad (a' > a).$$

32

In particular, when $F(t)$ is of exponential order e^{at} then it is also of exponential order $e^{a't}$, $(a' > a)$.

The familiar functions $\sin kt$, t^n, and e^{kt} are examples of functions of exponential order. In the cases of $\sin kt$ and t^n $(n \leq 0)$, we may take $t_0 = a = M = 1$ in applying the definition of exponential order. For the function t^n $(n > 0)$, a suitable t_0 can be found if a and M are any pair of positive constants. For e^{kt}, any non-negative constant will serve for t_0 if a is greater than or equal to k and $M = 1$. On the other hand, the function e^{t^2} is not of exponential order, for $e^{-at} e^{t^2} = e^{[t-(a/2)]^2} e^{-(a^2/4)}$ becomes infinite as t tends to infinity.

The fact that a function $F(t)$ is of exponential order is not alone sufficient to insure that it have a Laplace transform. This can be seen at once by considering the following example in which the integral fails to exist because of the behavior of the function in a neighborhood of $t = 0$.

Example 1. The function $F(t) = \dfrac{1}{t^2}$ does not have a transform.

To see that this is true, write formally,

$$\int_0^\infty e^{-st} t^{-2} \, dt = \int_0^1 e^{-st} t^{-2} \, dt + \int_1^\infty e^{-st} t^{-2} \, dt.$$

If we assume for the moment that the various integrals involved exist, for $0 < \varepsilon < 1$ we would have

$$\int_0^\infty e^{-st} t^{-2} \, dt \geq \int_0^1 e^{-st} t^{-2} \, dt = \lim_{\varepsilon \to 0} \int_\varepsilon^1 e^{-st} t^{-2} \, dt.$$

But when $s > 0$,

$$\int_0^1 e^{-st} t^{-2} \, dt > e^{-s} \int_\varepsilon^1 t^{-2} \, dt = e^{-s} \left[-\frac{1}{t} \right]_\varepsilon^1 = e^{-s} \left[\frac{1}{\varepsilon} - 1 \right].$$

Since $\lim_{\varepsilon \to 0} e^{-s} \left(\dfrac{1}{\varepsilon} - 1 \right) = \infty$, we see that $\int_0^1 e^{-st} t^{-2} \, dt$ diverges. This implies that $\int_0^\infty e^{-st} t^{-2} \, dt$ does not exist; that is, t^{-2} does not have a Laplace transform.

Therefore we shall impose an additional condition on $F(t)$. Before stating this condition, we introduce some convenient notation. By $F(t_i^+)$ we shall mean $\lim_{t \to t_i^+} F(t)$, where the plus sign on t_i^+ indicates that t is restricted to values greater than t_i in the limiting process. Similarly, by $F(t_i^-)$ we shall mean $\lim_{t \to t_i^-} F(t)$, where the minus sign on t_i^- indicates that t is restricted to values less than t_i in the limiting process. In particular, $F(0^+)$ means $\lim_{t \to 0^+} F(t)$. Note that the definition of these symbols does not assume that the function $F(t)$

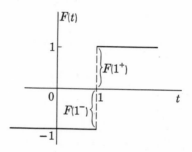

FIG. 3.   Illustration of a finite discontinuity.

is defined at t_i.   But we do assume that for some $\varepsilon > 0$ depending on t_i, the function $F(t)$ is defined whenever $0 < |t - t_i| < \varepsilon$, except at the origin where we assume definition in the range $0 < t < \varepsilon$ only.

A function $F(t)$ is said to have a *finite discontinuity* at $t = t_i$ if $F(t)$ is discontinuous at $t = t_i$ and if both $F(t_i^+)$ and $F(t_i^-)$ are finite. The difference $F(t_i^+) - F(t_i^-)$ is called the *jump* of $F(t)$ at $t = t_i$. A discontinuity at $t = 0$ is called finite if $F(0^+)$ is finite.

As an illustration of these definitions consider the function

$$(3) \qquad F(t) = \begin{cases} 1 & \text{for } t > 1, \\ -1 & \text{for } t < 1, \end{cases}$$

whose graph appears in Fig. 3. Note that this function is not defined at $t = 1$, but $F(t^+)$ and $F(t^-)$ exist for every value of t, including $t = 1$.   In fact $F(1^+) = 1$ and $F(1^-) = -1$.   Further, for $t \neq 1$, $F(t^+) = F(t^-)$. We conclude that the function $F(t)$ has a jump of 2 at $t = 1$ and is continuous elsewhere.

A function $F(t)$ is said to be *sectionally continuous* for $t \geq 0$ if it is continuous except for at most a finite number of finite discontinuities in the interval $0 \leq t \leq b$ for all $b > 0$. We shall always use the term *sectionally continuous* in the range $t \geq 0$ only. Thus in Fig. 4, the graph for $t < 0$ does not concern us here. This same example also illustrates the fact that a sectionally continuous function may have infinitely many finite discontinuities in an infinite interval, but it can have only a finite number in any finite interval $0 \leq t \leq b$ for all $b > 0$.

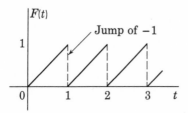

FIG. 4. Illustration of a sectionally continuous function.

Example 1 shows that if $F(t)$ is of exponential order but not sectionally continuous, it need not have a Laplace transform. Furthermore a function which is continuous but not of exponential order need not have a transform either, as may be seen from the following example.

look at

Example 2.   Let

(4)
$$F(t) = e^{t^2}.$$

Then
$$\int_0^\infty e^{-st} e^{t^2}\, dt = \lim_{b \to \infty} \int_0^b e^{-st} e^{t^2}\, dt.$$

But
$$\int_0^b e^{-st} e^{t^2}\, dt = e^{-(s^2/4)} \int_0^b e^{(t-s/2)^2}\, dt \geq e^{-(s^2/4)} \int_0^b dt = e^{-(s^2/4)} b,$$

and $\lim_{b \to \infty} e^{-(s^2/4)} b = \infty$. Therefore $\int_0^\infty e^{-st} e^{t^2}\, dt$ does not exist, and e^{t^2} does not have a Laplace transform.

The two preceding examples show that neither exponential order nor sectional continuity alone is sufficient to insure that $F(t)$ have a Laplace transform.   However, both conditions taken together do suffice, as will be shown in Theorem IV.

We now define a function $F(t)$ to be of class T if for some constant a it is of exponential order e^{at} and sectionally continuous.   We shall generally reserve the use of the letter a for the order constant.   It should be emphasized that these conditions are sufficient but not necessary, and there do exist functions which do not belong to class T yet do have a Laplace transform.   Example 3 illustrates such a function.   (See also Chapter 6.)

Example 3.   Let

(5) $$F(t) = 2te^{t^2} \cos e^{t^2}.$$

This function $F(t)$ is not of exponential order.   For as we have shown earlier, e^{t^2} is not of exponential order and for any given t_0 there is at least one value of t greater than t_0 such that $F(t) > e^{t^2}$.   Therefore $F(t)$ does not belong to class T.   However $F(t)$ does have a Laplace transform as we shall now show.   From the definition of $L\{F(t)\}$ we have

$$L\{F(t)\} = \int_0^\infty e^{-st}F(t)\,dt = \int_0^\infty e^{-st}2te^{t^2} \cos e^{t^2}\,dt.$$

Now if this last integral is integrated by parts, taking

$$u = e^{-st}, \qquad du = -se^{-st}\,dt,$$

$$dv = 2te^{t^2} \cos e^{t^2}\,dt, \qquad v = \sin e^{t^2},$$

then it becomes

$$L\{F(t)\} = e^{-st} \sin e^{t^2} \Big|_0^\infty + s\int_0^\infty e^{-st} \sin e^{t^2}\,dt$$

$$= -\sin 1 + s\int_0^\infty e^{-st} \sin e^{t^2}\,dt, \qquad (s > 0).$$

The existence of the last integral follows from its *absolute convergence.** Therefore $L\{2te^{t^2} \cos e^{t^2}\}$ exists.

In several theorems which follow we shall be concerned with the integration of a sectionally continuous function $G(t)$ over an interval of integration $a \le t \le b$ on which $G(t)$ may have a finite number of

---

* See Appendix III.

discontinuities which occur at the abscissas $t_1 < t_2 < \cdots < t_n$.
Then $\int_a^b G(t)\, dt$ is defined as the sum of integrals of the type

$$\int_{t_i}^{t_{i+1}} G(t)\, dt \equiv \lim_{\substack{\varepsilon_i \to 0 \\ \varepsilon_{i+1} \to 0}} \int_{t_i+\varepsilon_i}^{t_{i+1}-\varepsilon_{i+1}} G(t)\, dt,$$

where $\varepsilon_i > 0$ and $\varepsilon_{i+1} > 0$. That is,

$$\int_a^b G(t)\, dt = \sum_{i=0}^{n} \int_{t_i}^{t_{i+1}} G(t)\, dt, \qquad \text{where } t_0 = a \text{ and } t_{n+1} = b.$$

Theorem IV. *If $F(t)$ is a function of class T, then*   ✳ *read & know this*

$$L\{F(t)\} = \int_0^\infty e^{-st}\, F(t)\, dt$$

exists for $s > a$. In fact, $L\{|F(t)|\} = \int_0^\infty e^{-st}|F(t)|\, dt$ exists; that is,
$\int_0^\infty e^{-st} F(t)\, dt$ *is absolutely convergent, for $s > a$.*

Proof. Let the non-negative abscissas of the points of discontinuity be $t_1 < t_2 < t_3 < \cdots < t_n < \cdots$. Then we must prove the convergence of

$$(7) \qquad \int_0^\infty e^{-st} F(t)\, dt = \lim_{b \to \infty}\left[\int_0^{t_n} e^{-st} F(t)\, dt + \int_{t_n}^b e^{-st} F(t)\, dt\right],$$

where t_n is the abscissa of the last discontinuity in the interval $0 \le t \le b$. If no t_n exists, take $t_n = b$ in (7).

We first consider the integral

$$(8) \qquad \int_0^{t_n} e^{-st}|F(t)|\, dt = \sum_{i=0}^{n-1} \int_{t_i}^{t_{i+1}} e^{-st}|F(t)|\, dt, \qquad t_0 \equiv 0.$$

The fact that $F(t)$ is of exponential order and sectionally continuous implies the existence of a positive constant M such that $|F(t)| \le Me^{at}$ for all t such that $t_i < t < t_{i+1}$, $(i = 0, 1, \cdots)$. Hence each integral of the sum in (8) can be bounded as follows:

$$(9) \qquad \int_{t_i}^{t_{i+1}} e^{-st}|F(t)|\, dt \le \int_{t_i}^{t_{i+1}} Me^{-(s-a)t}\, dt = M\,\frac{e^{-(s-a)t}}{-(s-a)}\bigg]_{t_i}^{t_{i+1}}$$

$$= \frac{M}{s-a}\,[e^{-(s-a)t_i} - e^{-(s-a)t_{i+1}}], \qquad (s > a).$$

If we sum on both sides of (9) and observe that the terms on the right cancel in pairs except for the first and last, we get

(10) $$\int_0^{t_n} e^{-st}|F(t)|\,dt \leq \frac{M}{s-a}\left[e^{-(s-a)t_0} - e^{-(s-a)t_n}\right]$$

$$= \frac{M}{s-a}\left[1 - e^{-(s-a)t_n}\right]$$

for every n.   In a similar manner we have

(11) $$\int_{t_n}^{b} e^{-st}|F(t)|\,dt \leq \int_{t_n}^{b} Me^{-(s-a)t}\,dt = \frac{M}{s-a}\left[e^{-(s-a)t_n} - e^{-(s-a)b}\right].$$

Now, adding inequalities (10) and (11) we obtain

(12) $$\int_0^{b} e^{-st}|F(t)|\,dt \leq \frac{M}{s-a}\left[1 - e^{-(s-a)b}\right]$$

$$\leq \frac{M}{s-a}, \qquad (s > a).$$

Since the left-hand side of (12) is therefore a bounded monotonic non-decreasing function of b, we can infer* that $\int_0^{\infty} e^{-st}|F(t)|\,dt$ exists for $s > a$. This proves the absolute convergence of $\int_0^{\infty} e^{-st}F(t)\,dt$ which is a sufficient condition for the convergence† of $\int_0^{\infty} e^{-st}F(t)\,dt$.

EXERCISES I

1.   Find the Laplace transforms of:

(a) $F(t) = \begin{cases} 0, & (0 \leq t < 1), \\ t, & (t \geq 1). \end{cases}$

(b) $F(t) = \begin{cases} \cos t, & (0 \leq t < \pi), \\ 1, & (t \geq \pi). \end{cases}$

---

* See L. M. Graves, *The Theory of Functions of Real Variables* (New York, McGraw-Hill, 1946), p. 57.
† See D. V. Widder, *Advanced Calculus* (Englewood Cliffs, N.J., Prentice-Hall, 1947), p. 308.

did in class review

2. Show that $\lim_{t \to \infty} e^{-bt} F(t) = 0$ implies that $F(t)$ is of exponential order e^{bt}.

3. Examine each of the following functions for continuity, sectional continuity (compute the jumps), exponential order. Which are of class T?

$\mathcal{S}$ (a) $\dfrac{t^2}{t^2 + 3t + 2}$.   (e) $e^{-1/t} \, t^{-3/2}$.

no!
not sect.
cont.
(b) $\dfrac{t^2}{t^2 - 3t + 2}$.

(f) $F(t) = \begin{cases} \sin t, & (2n\pi \le t < (2n + 1)\pi), \\ 0, & ((2n + 1)\pi \le t < (2n + 2)\pi), \\ & (n = 0, 1, \cdots). \end{cases}$

(c) $\dfrac{t^{7/2} + 1}{t^4 + t^3}$.

(g) $F(t) = \begin{cases} \cos t, & (2n\pi \le t < (2n + 1)\pi), \\ 0, & ((2n + 1)\pi \le t < (2n + 2)\pi), \\ & (n = 0, 1, \cdots). \end{cases}$

(d) $te^{\sqrt{t}}$.   (h) $t^n F(t)$, where $F(t)$ is of class T, $(n \ge 0)$.

4. If $F(t)$ and $G(t)$ are both of class T, show that $F(t) + G(t)$ and $F(t)G(t)$ are of class T.

5. Show that if there exists a finite number a_0 such that $F(t)$ is of order $e^{(a_0 + \epsilon)t}$ for all $\epsilon > 0$, then $F(t)$ need *not* be of exponential order $e^{a_0 t}$.

6. If $F'(t)$ is continuous for $t \ge 0$ and if $L\{F(t)\}$ and $L\{F'(t)\}$ exist for $s = a$, show that $F(t)$ is of exponential order e^{at}, hence of class T.

2.3 TRANSFORMS OF DERIVATIVES

In §1.5 we proved a theorem concerning the Laplace transform of $F'(t)$. In that theorem the existence of $L\{F'(t)\}$ is assumed. In this section we first prove a theorem which yields the same formula for $L\{F'(t)\}$ but in which the conditions on $F(t)$ and $F'(t)$ are different. Then we extend our formula to cover a larger class of functions.

Theorem V. *Let*
(1) $F(t)$ *be continuous for* $t \ge 0$ *and of exponential order* e^{at},
(2) $F'(t)$ *be sectionally continuous.*

Then $L\{F'(t)\} = sL\{F(t)\} - F(0)$, $(s > a)$.

Proof. From definition we have

(1)
$$L\{F'(t)\} = \lim_{b \to \infty} \int_0^b e^{-st}F'(t)\, dt.$$

Now $F'(t)$ may have a finite number of discontinuities in the closed interval $[0,b]$. Let $t_1, t_2, \cdots, t_n$ be the positive abscissas of the points at which these discontinuities occur and order them as follows:

$$0 < t_1 < t_2 < \cdots < t_{n-1} < t_n \leq b.$$

Then

(2)
$$\int_0^b e^{-st}F'(t)\, dt = \int_0^{t_1} e^{-st}F'(t)\, dt + \int_{t_1}^{t_2} e^{-st}F'(t)\, dt + \cdots$$
$$+ \int_{t_n}^b e^{-st}F'(t)\, dt.$$

We now may integrate by parts in each term on the right-hand side of (2) to get

(3)
$$\int_0^b e^{-st}F'(t)\, dt = \left[e^{-st}F(t) \right]_{0^+}^{t_1^-}$$
$$+ \left[e^{-st}F(t) \right]_{t_1^+}^{t_2^-} + \cdots + \left[e^{-st}F(t) \right]_{t_n^+}^{b^-} + s \int_0^b e^{-st}F(t)\, dt.$$

Now by hypothesis (1), $F(t)$ is continuous, hence $F(t_i^+) = F(t_i^-)$ for $i = 1, 2, \cdots, n$. So

(4)
$$\int_0^b e^{-st}F'(t)\, dt = -F(0) + e^{-sb}F(b) + s \int_0^b e^{-st}F(t)\, dt.$$

Also by hypothesis (1), $F(t)$ is of exponential order e^{at}, hence $\lim_{b \to \infty} e^{-sb}F(b) = 0$ and $\lim_{b \to \infty} s \int_0^b e^{-st}F(t)\, dt = sL\{F(t)\}$, provided $s > a$. Therefore, if $s > a$, $\lim_{b \to \infty} \int_0^b e^{-st}F'(t)\, dt$ exists, and

(5)
$$L\{F'(t)\} = sL\{F(t)\} - F(0).$$

We now extend Theorem V to functions $F(t)$ with a finite number of finite discontinuities and exponential order, at the cost of additional terms in the formula for $L\{F'(t)\}$. These functions $F(t)$ are of course in class T.

look at proof

Theorem VI. *Let*
(1) *$F(t)$ be sectionally continuous with at most a finite number of discontinuities and of exponential order e^{at},*
(2) *$F'(t)$ be sectionally continuous.*
Then

$$L\{F'(t)\} = sL\{F(t)\} - F(0^+) - \sum_{i=1}^{n} e^{-st_i}\,[F(t_i^+) - F(t_i^-)], \quad (s > a),$$

where $t_1, t_2, \cdots, t_n$ are the positive abscissas of the points of discontinuity of $F(t)$.

Proof. By steps similar to those that led to equation (3) in the proof of Theorem V, we obtain under our present hypotheses the equation

$$(6) \qquad \int_0^b e^{-st}F'(t)\,dt = \left[e^{-st}F(t)\right]_0^{\tau_1^-} + \left[e^{-st}F(t)\right]_{\tau_1^+}^{\tau_2^-} + \cdots$$

$$+ \left[e^{-st}F(t)\right]_{\tau_m^+}^{b^-} + s\int_0^b e^{-st}F(t)\,dt$$

$$= -F(0^+) + e^{-sb}F(b^-) + s\int_0^b e^{-st}F(t)\,dt$$

$$- \sum_{j=1}^{m} e^{-s\tau_j}\,[F(\tau_j^+) - F(\tau_j^-)],$$

where $\tau_1, \tau_2, \cdots, \tau_m$ are the positive abscissas of the points of discontinuity of $F'(t)$ between 0 and b.   If $F(t)$ is continuous at one of the abscissas τ_j, the corresponding term of the sum is zero.   But if $\tau_j = t_i$, so that one of the points of discontinuity of $F'(t)$ is also a point of discontinuity of $F(t)$, the term becomes $e^{-st_i}\,[F(t_i^+) - F(t_i^-)]$.   Hence, letting $b \to \infty$ in (6) we obtain

$$(7) \qquad \int_0^\infty e^{-st}F'(t)\,dt = -F(0^+) + s\int_0^\infty e^{-st}F(t)\,dt$$

$$- \lim_{b \to \infty} \sum_{i=1}^{m'} e^{-st_i}[F(t_i^+) - F(t_i^-)],$$

where $t_1, t_2, \cdots, t_{m'}$, are the positive abscissas of the discontinuities of $F(t)$ between 0 and b.   Since $F(t)$ has only a finite number of finite discontinuities, the sum

$$\sum_{i=1}^{m'} e^{-st_i}[F(t_i^+) - F(t_i^-)]$$

has the limit

$$\sum_{i=1}^{n} e^{-st_i}[F(t_i^{+}) - F(t_i^{-})].$$

Hence the theorem is proved.

EXERCISES 2

1. If $F(t) = \begin{cases} 0, & (0 \leq t < \pi), \\ \sin t, & (t \geq \pi), \end{cases}$ use Theorem V to find $L\{F'(t)\}$. Check by transforming directly.

2. Use the results of 1(b) Exercises 1 and Theorem VI to find the Laplace transform of

$$F(t) = \begin{cases} -\sin t, & (0 \leq t < \pi), \\ 0, & (t \geq \pi). \end{cases}$$

Check by transforming directly.

2.4 THE CONVOLUTION INTEGRAL

Let $F(t)$ and $G(t)$ be any two functions of class T. Then the function of t defined by

(1) $$F * G \equiv \int_{0}^{t} F(\tau)G(t - \tau) \, d\tau$$

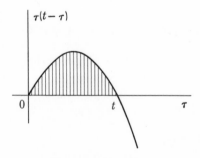

FIG. 5. Shaded area $= t * t$.

is called the *convolution of F(t) and G(t)*.   If we replace the variable τ through the substitution $u = t - \tau$, we get

$$F * G = \int_0^t G(u)F(t - u)\, du = G * F.$$

Thus the process of convolution is commutative: $F * G = G * F$.

As an illustration of the convolution integral, consider the following example.

Example 1.   Let $F(t) = e^{-at}$ and $G(t) = \sin bt$.

Then

$$F * G = \int_0^t e^{-a\tau} \sin b(t - \tau)\, d\tau = \int_0^t e^{-a(t-\tau)} \sin b\tau\, d\tau,$$

where we have used the fact that $F * G = G * F$.   Then

$$F * G = e^{-at} \int_0^t e^{a\tau} \sin b\tau\, d\tau = \frac{e^{a(\tau - t)}}{a^2 + b^2} (a \sin b\tau - b \cos b\tau) \Big|_0^t$$

$$= \frac{1}{a^2 + b^2} [a \sin bt - b \cos bt + be^{-at}].$$

Now we know that $F(t)$, $G(t)$, and the sum of the functions on the right-hand side have transforms. The relation among these transforms is given by the Convolution Theorem which we shall prove after stating a preliminary lemma on the nature of $F * G$.

Lemma.   *If F(t) and G(t) are of class T, then F * G is of class T.*

We leave as an exercise the proof of the fact that $F * G$ has exponential order $e^{(c+\varepsilon)t}$, where e^{ct} is the maximum of the orders of F and G and ε is any positive number.   The continuity of $F * G$ follows from a more general lemma discussed in Chapter 6.   Our present lemma thus guarantees the existence of $L\{F * G\}$ whenever $F(t)$ and $G(t)$ are of class T.

Theorem VII.   *Convolution Theorem.   If F(t) and G(t) are of class T, then*

(2) $$L\{F * G\} = f(s)g(s), \qquad (s > a),$$

where e^{at} is the maximum of the exponential orders of F(t) and G(t).

Proof. The basic idea of the proof originates from the fact that by definition

$$f(s)g(s) = \left(\int_0^\infty e^{-st}F(t)\,dt \right)\left(\int_0^\infty e^{-st}G(t)\,dt \right),$$

which, suggests consideration of a double integral of the form

$$(3) \qquad I(A) = \iint_A e^{-s(x+y)}F(x)G(y)\,dx\,dy$$

$$= \int_0^K e^{-sx}F(x)\,dx \int_0^K e^{-sy}G(y)\,dy.$$

The region A of integration is illustrated in Fig. 6. Clearly the

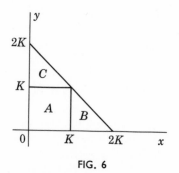

FIG. 6

$\lim\limits_{K \to \infty} I(A) = f(s)g(s)$.   Hence, if we can show that the first integral in (3) has $L\{F * G\}$ as its limit, then the theorem will be proved.

We note that the lemma implies the existence of

$$(4) \quad L\{F * G\} = \lim_{K \to \infty} \int_0^{2K} e^{-st}\left(\int_0^t F(x)G(t-x)\,dx \right) dt, \qquad (s > a).$$

The latter integral is equal to a double integral over the triangular region illustrated in Fig. 7 and therefore may be written in the form

$$(5) \qquad \int_0^{2K} F(x)\,dx \int_x^{2K} e^{-st}G(t-x)\,dt$$

by interchanging the order of integration. Now, if we replace the variable of integration t by $y = t - x$, we get

$$\int_0^{2K} F(x)\, dx \int_x^{2K} e^{-st} G(t-x)\, dt = \int_0^{2K} F(x)\, dx \int_0^{2K-x} e^{-s(x+y)} G(y)\, dy$$

$$= \int\!\!\int_R e^{-s(x+y)} F(x)G(y)\, dx\, dy = I(R),$$

where the region of integration R is composed of the three domains

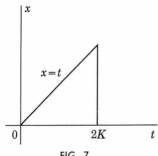

FIG. 7

A, B, and C as shown in Fig. 6.   If we can show that $\lim\limits_{K \to \infty} I(B) = \lim\limits_{K \to \infty} I(C) = 0$, the proof will be complete, for $I(R) = I(A) + I(B) + I(C)$, hence $L\{F * G\} = \lim\limits_{K \to \infty} I(R) = \lim\limits_{K \to \infty} I(A) = f(s)g(s)$.   To show that $\lim\limits_{K \to \infty} I(B) = 0$, we consider

$$I(B) = \int\!\!\int_B e^{-s(x+y)} F(x)G(y)\, dx\, dy.$$

Making use of Fig. 6 to determine the limits of integration, we may write

$$|I(B)| \leq \int\!\!\int_B e^{-s(x+y)} |F(x)|\, |G(y)|\, dx\, dy$$

$$= \int_0^K e^{-sy} |G(y)|\, dy \int_K^{2K-y} e^{-sx} |F(x)|\, dx$$

$$\leq \int_0^K e^{-sy} |G(y)|\, dy \int_K^{2K} e^{-sx} |F(x)|\, dx.$$

Now the convergence of $\int_0^\infty e^{-sx}|F(x)|\,dx$ for $s > a$ implies* that $\lim\limits_{K \to \infty} \int_K^{2K} e^{-sx}|F(x)|\,dx = 0$. This, together with the existence of $L\{|G(t)|\}$, implies that $\lim\limits_{K \to \infty} I(B) = 0$. A similar argument proves that $\lim\limits_{K \to \infty} I(C) = 0$.

This theorem has many applications. One of its principal uses in this text is to find inverses of transforms. That is, if the inverses of $f(s)$ and $g(s)$ are known, then the convolution integral gives the inverse of the product $f(s)g(s)$. For this purpose it is more convenient to write (2) in the form

$$(6) \qquad L^{-1}\{f(s)g(s)\} = F * G = \int_0^t F(\tau)G(t - \tau)\,d\tau.$$

The next two examples illustrate this application.

Example 2. Find the inverse of $\dfrac{1}{s^3 - ks^2}$.

We think of this function written in the form $\dfrac{1}{s^2} \cdot \dfrac{1}{s - k}$ and take $f(s) = \dfrac{1}{s^2}$ and $g(s) = \dfrac{1}{s - k}$. Then by (6),

$$L^{-1}\left\{\frac{1}{s^3 - ks^2}\right\} = t * e^{kt} = \int_0^t \tau e^{k(t-\tau)}\,d\tau$$

$$= e^{kt}\int_0^t \tau e^{-k\tau}\,d\tau = -\frac{e^{kt}}{k^2}\left[(k\tau + 1)e^{-k\tau}\right]_0^t$$

$$= \frac{1}{k^2}(e^{kt} - kt - 1).$$

Example 3. Find the inverse of $\dfrac{1}{(s^2 + k^2)^2}$.

This time we take $\qquad f(s) = g(s) = \dfrac{1}{s^2 + k^2}$

so that

$$F(t) = G(t) = \frac{1}{k}\sin kt.$$

* See Appendix III, definition of convergence of improper integrals.

Then

$$L^{-1}\left\{\frac{1}{(s^2+k^2)^2}\right\} = \frac{1}{k}\sin kt * \frac{1}{k}\sin kt = \frac{1}{k^2}\int_0^t \sin k\tau \sin k(t-\tau)\,d\tau$$

$$= \frac{1}{k^2}\int_0^t \sin k\tau\,(\sin kt \cos k\tau - \cos kt \sin k\tau)\,d\tau$$

$$= \frac{1}{k^2}\left[\sin kt \int_0^t \sin k\tau \cos k\tau\,d\tau\right.$$

$$\left. - \cos kt \int_0^t \sin^2 k\tau\,d\tau\right]$$

$$= \frac{1}{k^2}\left[\sin kt\,\frac{(1-\cos 2kt)}{4k}\right.$$

$$\left. - \cos kt\left(\frac{t}{2} - \frac{1}{4k}\sin 2kt\right)\right]$$

$$= \frac{1}{4k^3}[\sin kt - \sin kt \cos 2kt - 2kt \cos kt$$

$$+ \cos kt \sin 2kt].$$

Combining the second and fourth terms we have

$$L^{-1}\left\{\frac{1}{(s^2+k^2)^2}\right\} = \frac{1}{2k^3}[\sin kt - kt \cos kt].$$

We can easily prove the following corollary to the Convolution Theorem.

Corollary. *Integration of $F(t)$ with respect to t over the interval $(0, t)$ is reflected in division of the transform $f(s)$ by s, that is,*

$$(7) \qquad L\left\{\int_0^t F(\tau)\,d\tau\right\} = \frac{1}{s}f(s), \qquad (s > \tfrac{1}{2}(a+|a|)).$$

Proof. If in the convolution integral (1) we set $G(t) \equiv 1$ and use the Convolution Theorem, we get (7).

Example 4. Apply the corollary to find $L^{-1}\left\{\dfrac{1}{s^3+k^2s}\right\}$, $(s > 0)$.

$$L^{-1}\left\{\frac{1}{s^3+k^2s}\right\} = L^{-1}\left\{\frac{1}{s}\frac{1}{s^2+k^2}\right\} = \int_0^t \frac{1}{k}\sin kt\,dt = \frac{1}{k^2}\left[-\cos kt\right]_0^t$$

$$= \frac{1-\cos kt}{k^2}.$$

It is sometimes convenient to express a transform as a product of three factors, say $f(s)g(s)h(s)$. In this case an extension of the Convolution Theorem is useful in finding the inverse transform. If we have three functions $F(t)$, $G(t)$, and $H(t)$, each of which satisfies the hypotheses of the Convolution Theorem, then

$$(8)\ f(s)(g(s)h(s)) = L\{F(t) * L^{-1}\{g(s)h(s)\}\} = L\{F(t) * (G(t) * H(t))\}.$$

However, the left-hand side of (8) is also equal to $(f(s)g(s))h(s)$, and

$$(f(s)g(s))h(s) = L\{L^{-1}\{f(s)g(s)\} * H(t)\} = L\{(F(t) * G(t)) * H(t)\}.$$

Thus we may write

$$f(s)g(s)h(s) = L\{F(t) * G(t) * H(t)\}$$

unambiguously, where

$$F * G * H = \int_0^t F(x)\, dx \int_0^y G(y - x)H(t - y)\, dy.$$

Of course there are several other integral forms equivalent to this one.

Example 5. Apply (8) to find the inverse transform of $\dfrac{1}{s^2} f(s)$.

Setting $g(s) = h(s) = \dfrac{1}{s}$ in (8) we get

$$(9)\qquad \frac{1}{s^2}f(s) = L\{F(t) * 1 * 1\} = L\left\{\int_0^t F(\tau)\, d\tau * 1\right\}$$

$$= L\left\{\int_0^t du \int_0^u F(\tau)\, d\tau\right\}.$$

In particular, for $f(s) = \dfrac{1}{s - k}$, (9) gives

$$L^{-1}\left\{\frac{1}{s^2(s - k)}\right\} = \int_0^t du \int_0^u e^{k\tau}\, d\tau = \int_0^t \frac{1}{k}\, [e^{ku} - 1]\, du$$

$$= \frac{1}{k}\left[\frac{e^{ku}}{k} - u\right]_0^t = \frac{1}{k}\left[\frac{e^{kt} - 1}{k} - t\right].$$

EXERCISES 3

1. Compute $F * G$ and $G * F$ in each case:

(a) $F(t) = t$, $G(t) = t$.

(b) $F(t) = e^t$, $G(t) = e^{-t}$.

(c) $F(t) = 1$, $G(t) = t^n$, $(n \geq 0)$.

2. Apply the Convolution Theorem to find the inverse transforms of the following:

(a) $\dfrac{1}{s^2}$.

(d) $\dfrac{s}{(s + 1)(s^2 + 1)}$.

(b) $\dfrac{1}{s(s + 1)}$.

(e) $\dfrac{s^2}{(s^2 + k^2)^2}$.

(c) $\dfrac{1}{(s - a)(s - b)}$.

(f) $\dfrac{k}{(s + a)[(s - a)^2 + k^2]}$.

3. Use the corollary to the Convolution Theorem to find the inverses of the following transforms:

(a) $\dfrac{1}{s(s^2 - k^2)}$.

(b) $\dfrac{1}{s^2(s^2 + k^2)}$.

4. Prove that if the class T functions $F(t)$ and $G(t)$ are of exponential order e^{at} and e^{bt} respectively, then $F * G$ is of exponential order $e^{(c+\varepsilon)t}$, where c is the maximum of a and b, and ε is any positive number.

2.5 INTEGRAL EQUATIONS

An equation in which an unknown function occurs under a definite integral sign is called an *integral equation*. Also, in some applications, the unknown function occurs not only under the integral sign but in differentiated form in other terms of the same equation. In such a case the equation is called an *integrodifferential equation*. In either case, if the definite integral is of the convolution type, then the Convolution Theorem may enable us to transform such an equation into an algebraic equation in the transform function. We shall proceed formally.

To illustrate an integral equation in which the integral is of the convolution type, we consider the general equation of the form

$$(1) \qquad X(t) = F(t) + \int_0^t G(t - \tau)X(\tau)\, d\tau,$$

in which F and G are known functions and we seek a function $X(t)$ for which (1) is true. Under the assumption that the functions in (1) have transforms, we have

$$x(s) = f(s) + g(s)x(s),$$

which when solved for $x(s)$ gives

$$(2) \qquad x(s) = \frac{f(s)}{1 - g(s)}.$$

This is the transform of the solution function $X(t)$ of (1). To find $X(t)$ explicitly we must now find $L^{-1}\{x(s)\}$. This procedure is carried out in the next example.

Example 1. Find $X(t)$ such that

$$X(t) = t^3 + \int_0^t X(\tau)\sin(t - \tau)\, d\tau.$$

The transformed equation is

$$x(s) = \frac{6}{s^4} + \frac{x(s)}{s^2 + 1},$$

which when solved for $x(s)$ gives

$$x(s) = \frac{6}{s^4} + \frac{6}{s^6}.$$

Therefore the solution function is

$$X(t) = t^3 + \frac{t^5}{20}.$$

One of the simpler illustrations of an integrodifferential equation comes from the field of electrical engineering.* For those familiar with this field, it is well known that the current $I(t)$ in a single loop R-L-C circuit satisfies the equation

$$(3) \qquad L\frac{dI(t)}{dt} + RI(t) + \frac{1}{C}\int_0^t I(\tau)\, d\tau = E(t)$$

* See Appendix IV.

where R, L, and C are constants and $E(t)$ is a given "driving" function. This equation may be converted into an algebraic equation in the transform $i(s) = L\{I(t)\}$ by taking the Laplace transform of both sides. That is,

$$(4) \qquad L[si(s) - I_0] + Ri(s) + \frac{1}{C}\frac{i(s)}{s} = e(s),$$

where $I_0 = I(0)$. Clearly if the constants R, L, and C are given and the function $E(t)$ is such as to have a transform, we may solve equation (4) for $i(s)$. Then to obtain the current $I(t)$, we must find $L^{-1}\{i(s)\}$.

Example 2.   Use the Laplace transform method to solve

$$.01\frac{dI}{dt} + 10I + 2500\int_0^t I(\tau)\,d\tau = 30,$$

given $I(0) = 0$.

The transformed equation is

$$.01si(s) + 10i(s) + \frac{2500i(s)}{s} = \frac{30}{s}.$$

Hence
$$i(s) = \frac{3000}{(s + 500)^2},$$

and
$$I(t) = 3000te^{-500t}.$$

EXERCISES 4

1. Solve for $X(t)$:
$$X(t) = 1 + a\int_0^t X(\tau)\,d\tau.$$

2. Solve for $X(t)$:
$$X(t) = \cos t + \int_0^t X(\tau)e^{-(t-\tau)}\,d\tau.$$

3. Solve for $X(t)$:
$$\left\{\begin{array}{l} \dfrac{d}{dt}X(t) = a - a^2\displaystyle\int_0^t X(\tau)\,d\tau, \\[2mm] X(0) = 0. \end{array}\right.$$

4. Given $H(t)$ of class T, show that the integral equation

$$X(t) = H(t) + \int_0^t X(\tau) \sin (t - \tau) \, d\tau$$

has a solution expressible in terms of $H(t)$ of the form

$$X(t) = H(t) + \int_0^t \int_0^\tau H(u)\, du \, d\tau.$$

Apply this result to solve

$$X(t) = \cos kt + \int_0^t X(\tau) \sin (t - \tau) \, d\tau.$$

2.6 DIFFERENTIATION OF TRANSFORMS

The proof of the existence of the Laplace transform of functions of class T given in Theorem IV shows that the transform of the absolute value of $F(t)$, and hence of $F(t)$ itself, converges independently of the value of s in the range $s \geq b$, where b is any constant greater than a. This is also expressed by saying that $L\{F(t)\}$ *converges uniformly*† for $s \geq b > a$. This property, namely the uniform convergence of $L\{F(t)\}$, justifies the interchange of certain operations which we shall assume to be valid and apply subsequently.‡ Thus, when $F(t)$ is of class T:

(1) $$\lim_{s \to \infty} \int_0^\infty e^{-st} F(t) \, dt = \int_0^\infty \lim_{s \to \infty} [e^{-st} F(t)] \, dt.$$

(2) $$\lim_{s \to 0^+} \int_0^\infty e^{-st} F(t) \, dt = \int_0^\infty \lim_{s \to 0^+} [e^{-st} F(t)] \, dt, \qquad (a < 0).$$

(3) $$\frac{d}{ds} \int_0^\infty e^{-st} F(t) \, dt = \int_0^\infty \frac{d}{ds} [e^{-st} F(t)] \, dt.$$

(4) $$\int_s^c ds \int_0^\infty e^{-st} F(t) \, dt = \int_0^\infty dt \int_s^c e^{-st} F(t) \, ds.$$

---

† See Appendix III.

‡ Cf. D. V. Widder, *Advanced Calculus* (Englewood Cliffs, N.J., Prentice Hall 1945), Chapter X. We speak interchangeably of the convergence of $L\{F(t)\}$ and its defining integral.

In equation (3), the fact that $-tF(t)$ is again of class T (see 4, Exercises 1) implies that $\int_0^\infty \dfrac{d}{ds} (e^{-st}F(t))\, dt$ exists and converges uniformly and the range is still $s \geq b > a$. As an immediate application of property (3) we prove the following theorem.

Theorem VIII. *Differentiation of $f(s)$. If $f(s) = L\{F(t)\}$ where $F(t)$ is of class T, then*

$$(5) \qquad \frac{d^n}{ds^n} f(s) = L\{(-1)^n t^n F(t)\}, \qquad (s > a).$$

Proof. It follows from (3), that

$$\frac{d}{ds} f(s) = \frac{d}{ds} \int_0^\infty e^{-st} F(t)\, dt = \int_0^\infty \frac{d}{ds} [e^{-st} F(t)]\, dt = \int_0^\infty e^{-st} [-tF(t)]\, dt$$

$$= L\{-tF(t)\}.$$

Hence the theorem follows by repeated application of (3) and 3(h), Exercises 1.

It should be noted that use of the Laplace transform method of solution of a differential equation in which the coefficients are polynomials in the independent variable does not lead to an algebraic equation.   In fact, the transform of such an equation leads to another ordinary differential equation in which the value of the transform function is the dependent variable and s is the independent variable. To illustrate, consider the following differential equation (Bessel's equation of order zero):

$$tX''(t) + X'(t) + tX(t) = 0.$$

If we formally take the transform of both sides of this equation and make use of Theorem VIII, we get

$$-\frac{d}{ds} [s^2 x(s) - sX(0) - X'(0)] + sx(s) - X(0) - \frac{d}{ds} x(s) = 0,$$

which reduces to

$$(s^2 + 1)x'(s) + sx(s) = 0,$$

an ordinary differential equation for the determination of the transform function $x(s)$. The solution of this equation is

$$\ln x(s) = -\tfrac{1}{2} \ln (s^2 + 1) + C,$$

or

$$x(s) = \frac{k}{\sqrt{s^2 + 1}},$$

where C and k are constants of integration which are related by the equation $C = \ln k$. Now the function $x(s)$ may be written

$$x(s) = ks^{-1}\left[1 + \frac{1}{s^2}\right]^{-1/2}$$

$$= \frac{k}{s}\left[1 - \frac{1}{2}\cdot\frac{1}{s^2} + \frac{1}{2}\cdot\frac{3}{2}\cdot\frac{1}{2}\cdot\frac{1}{s^4} + \cdots\right.$$

$$\left. + \frac{1\cdot 3\cdot 5\cdots(2n-1)\,(-1)^n}{2^n n!}\frac{}{s^{2n}} + \cdots\right]$$

$$= k\sum_{n=0}^{\infty}\frac{1\cdot 3\cdot 5\cdots(2n-1)\,(-1)^n}{2^n n!}\frac{}{s^{2n+1}}$$

$$= k\sum_{n=0}^{\infty}\frac{(2n)!}{2^{2n}(n!)^2}\frac{(-1)^n}{s^{2n+1}}.$$

If we take the inverse transform of $x(s)$ term by term, we get

$$X(t) = L^{-1}\{x(s)\} = L^{-1}\left\{k\sum_{n=0}^{\infty}\frac{(2n)!}{2^{2n}(n!)^2}\frac{(-1)^n}{s^{2n+1}}\right\}$$

$$= k\sum_{n=0}^{\infty}\frac{(2n)!(-1)^n}{2^{2n}(n!)^2}L^{-1}\left\{\frac{1}{s^{2n+1}}\right\}$$

$$= k\sum_{n=0}^{\infty}\frac{(-1)^n t^{2n}}{2^{2n}(n!)^2}.$$

The function $\dfrac{1}{k} X(t)$ is usually denoted by $J_0(t)$.

The justification for taking the inverse transform in the above series is given by the following theorem.

Theorem IX. *Let the series*

(6) $$f(s) \equiv \sum_{k=0}^{\infty} A_k \frac{1}{s^{k+1}}$$

converge for $s > a > 0$. *Then an inverse transform of* $f(s)$ *is given by the series*

(7) $$F(t) \equiv \sum_{k=0}^{\infty} A_k \frac{t^k}{k!}, \qquad (s > a, t \geq 0).$$

Furthermore, (7) *converges absolutely and uniformly† in every closed interval* $0 \leq t \leq R$.

Proof. We first show that $\sum_{k=0}^{\infty} A_k \dfrac{t^k}{k!}$ converges absolutely and uniformly. Let $\bar{a}$ be a number such that $s > \bar{a} > a$. Then $\lim_{k \to \infty} A_k \dfrac{1}{\bar{a}^{k+1}} = 0$. Hence the numbers $A_k \dfrac{1}{\bar{a}^{k+1}}$, $k = 0, 1, \cdots$ are bounded, say by M. Thus the convergence of (6) implies the existence of constants $M > 0$ and $\bar{a} > a$ such that $|A_k| \leq M\bar{a}^{k+1}$ for all $k \geq 0$. Then for $0 \leq t \leq R$,

$$\left| A_k \frac{t^k}{k!} \right| = |A_k| \frac{t^k}{k!} \leq M\bar{a} \frac{(\bar{a}t)^k}{k!} \leq M\bar{a} \frac{(\bar{a}R)^k}{k!}.$$

Since the series of constants $\sum_{k=0}^{\infty} M\bar{a} \dfrac{(\bar{a}R)^k}{k!}$ converges to $M\bar{a}e^{\bar{a}R}$, the series $\sum_{k=0}^{\infty} A_k \dfrac{t^k}{k!}$ converges absolutely and uniformly by comparison, and $F(t)$ is of exponential order $e^{\bar{a}t}$. Since a power series is continuous‡ in its interval of convergence, we have that $F(t)$ is of class T, hence by Theorem IV we know that $L\{|F(t)|\}$ exists. Furthermore, because $e^{-st} \leq 1$, the series $\sum_{k=0}^{\infty} e^{-st} A_k \dfrac{t^k}{k!}$ is also uniformly convergent, hence we can integrate it term by term and show that

† See Appendix III.
‡ cf. D. V. Widder, *Advanced Calculus* (Englewood Cliffs, N.J., Prentice-Hall, 1947), p. 257.

$L\{F(t)\} = f(s)$ is given by (6).   For we have

$$\left| \int_0^R e^{-st} \sum_{k=0}^\infty A_k \frac{t^k}{k!}\, dt - \sum_{k=0}^n \frac{A_k}{k!} \int_0^R e^{-st} t^k\, dt \right| = \left| \sum_{k=n+1}^\infty \frac{A_k}{k!} \int_0^R e^{-st} t^k\, dt \right|$$

$$\leq \sum_{k=n+1}^\infty \frac{|A_k|}{k!} \int_0^\infty e^{-st} t^k\, dt \leq M \sum_{k=n+1}^\infty \left(\frac{\bar{a}}{s}\right)^{k+1}.$$

This inequality is true for all R and n, so first letting R approach infinity we obtain

$$\left| L\{F(t)\} - \sum_{k=0}^n \frac{A_k}{k!} \frac{k!}{s^{k+1}} \right| \leq M \sum_{k=n+1}^\infty \left(\frac{\bar{a}}{s}\right)^{k+1}.$$

Then, letting n go to infinity we have $|L\{F(t)\} - f(s)| = 0$, that is, $L\{F(t)\} = f(s)$.

EXERCISES 5

1.   Use the fact that $f'(s) = -L\{tF(t)\}$ to find the inverse transform of $s/(s^2 + 1)^2$.   Verify by use of the Convolution Theorem.

2.   Show that under suitable assumptions the following are true:

(a) $L\{tX(t)\} = -x'(s)$.

(b) $L\{tX'(t)\} = -sx'(s) - x(s)$.

(c) $L\{tX''(t)\} = -s^2 x'(s) - 2sx(s) + X(0)$.

3.   Use the Laplace transform method to find solutions for each of the following:

(a) $tX''(t) + (t + 1)X'(t) + X(t) = t + \frac{1}{2}$.

(b) $tX''(t) + (3t - 1)X'(t) - (4t + 9)X(t) = 0, \qquad X(0) = 0$.

(c) $tX''(t) + (t - 1)X'(t) - X(t) = 0, \qquad X(0) = 0$.

4.   Show that by termwise inversion of a suitable series in powers of $\frac{1}{s}$ one obtains:

(a) $L^{-1}\left\{ \ln\left(1 + \frac{1}{s}\right) \right\} = \dfrac{1 - e^{-t}}{t}$.

(b) $L^{-1}\left\{ \dfrac{1}{s} e^{-1/s} \right\} = J_0(2\sqrt{t})$.

5. Solve by use of Laplace transforms:

$$tX''(t) + X'(t) - tX(t) = 0, \qquad X(0) = 1.$$

2.7 INTEGRATION OF TRANSFORMS

A theorem on the integration of transforms follows directly from properties (1), (4), §2.6.

Theorem X. *If* $\dfrac{F(t)}{t}$ *is of class T and if* $f(s) = L\{F(t)\}$ *(with* $F(t)$ *of exponential order* e^{at}*), then*

(1)
$$\int_s^\infty f(s) \, ds = L\left\{\frac{F(t)}{t}\right\}, \qquad (s > a).$$

Proof. From the definition of the Laplace transform we have

$$f(s) = \int_0^\infty e^{-st} F(t) \, dt.$$

Then integrating both sides with respect to s over the range (s, ∞) and making use of properties (1), (4), §2.6, we have

$$\int_s^\infty f(s) \, ds = \int_s^\infty ds \int_0^\infty e^{-st} F(t) \, dt = \lim_{c \to \infty} \int_0^\infty dt \int_s^c e^{-st} F(t) \, ds$$

$$= \int_0^\infty \left[\frac{e^{-st}}{-t} F(t)\right]_s^\infty dt = \int_0^\infty e^{-st}\left(\frac{F(t)}{t}\right) dt = L\left\{\frac{F(t)}{t}\right\}.$$

Corollary. *If* $\dfrac{F(t)}{t}$ *is of class T and* $a < 0$*, then*

(2)
$$\int_0^\infty \frac{F(t)}{t} \, dt = \int_0^\infty f(s) \, ds.$$

Proof. By Theorem X, $\displaystyle\int_0^\infty e^{-st} \frac{F(t)}{t} \, dt = \int_s^\infty f(x) \, dx.$ Now making use of property (2), §2.6, which holds since $a < 0$, we have

$$\lim_{s \to 0^+} \int_s^\infty f(x) \, dx = \lim_{s \to 0^+} \int_0^\infty e^{-st} \frac{F(t)}{t} \, dt = \int_0^\infty \frac{F(t)}{t} \, dt.$$

By property (3), §2.6, it follows that $f(s)$ must be continuous for

$s > a$. Hence the first integral is a continuous function of its lower limit s for $s > a$ and therefore the limit is equal to $\int_0^\infty f(x)\,dx$.

EXERCISES 6

1. Show that:

(a) $L\left\{\dfrac{\sin kt}{t}\right\} = \cot^{-1}\dfrac{s}{k}$.

(b) $L\left\{\dfrac{1 - \cos kt}{t}\right\} = \dfrac{1}{2}\,\ln\left(1 + \dfrac{k^2}{s^2}\right)$.

2. Show that:

(a) $\displaystyle\int_0^\infty \frac{\sin kt}{t}\,dt = \int_0^\infty \frac{k}{s^2 + k^2}\,ds = \frac{\pi}{2}$.

(b) $\displaystyle\int_0^\infty \frac{e^{-t} - e^{-nt}}{t}\,dt = \ln n$, $(n > 0)$.

(c) $\displaystyle\int_0^\infty \frac{e^{-at}\sin bt}{t}\,dt = \tan^{-1}\frac{b}{a}$.

3. Use 1(a) to show that

$$L\{Si(t)\} = \frac{1}{s}\tan^{-1} s$$

where $Si(t) = \displaystyle\int_t^\infty \frac{\sin u}{u}\,du$. $Si(t)$ is called the "sine integral," and can be shown to be of class T.

2.8 SOME SPECIAL LIMITS

Sometimes certain properties of the Laplace transform concerned with initial and final values are helpful.   For example, we may want to determine the behavior of $F(t)$ as t becomes large without actually knowing $F(t)$.   This can often be done if we know the transform $f(s)$.   Several properties which are useful in this respect are embodied in the following theorem.

Theorem XI.   *If $F(t)$ is of class T and $f(s) = L\{F(t)\}$, then:*
(a) $\lim\limits_{s\to\infty} L\{t^n F(t)\} = 0$, $(n = 0, 1, 2, \cdots)$, and *in particular* $\lim\limits_{s\to\infty} L\{F(t)\} = \lim\limits_{s\to\infty} f(s) = 0$;

(b) If $a < 0$, $\lim\limits_{s\to 0^+} f(s) = \int_0^\infty F(t)\, dt$;

(c) *If $F(t)$ has at most a finite number of discontinuities at $t_1, t_2, \cdots, t_m$ and $F'(t)$ is of class T, then*

(1) $\lim\limits_{s\to\infty} sf(s) = F(0^+)$,

(2) $\lim\limits_{s\to 0^+} sf(s) = \lim\limits_{t\to\infty} F(t) + \sum\limits_{i=1}^m [F(t_i{}^+) - F(t_i{}^-)]$, *if $a < 0$ and either limit exists.*

Proof.   *(a)* Since $F(t)$ is of class T, it is true that $t^n F(t)$, $(n = 0, 1, 2, \cdots)$, is also of class T.   Therefore, we may use property (1), §2.6, to get

(1) $\lim\limits_{s\to\infty} L\{t^n F(t)\} = \int_0^\infty \lim\limits_{s\to\infty} (e^{-st} F(t) t^n)\, dt = 0$, $(n = 0, 1, 2, \cdots)$.

(b) Since $f(s)$ is continuous for $s > a$, and $a < 0$, we have by direct use of (2), §2.6, that $\lim\limits_{s\to 0^+} f(s)$ exists and equals $\int_0^\infty F(t)\, dt$.

(c) Under the additional hypothesis given in *(c)* in the statement of the theorem we know that Theorem VI is applicable and gives

(2) $sf(s) = L\{F'(t)\} + F(0^+) + \sum\limits_{i=1}^m e^{-st_i}[F(t_i{}^+) - F(t_i{}^-)]$.

Hence,

$$(3) \qquad \lim_{s \to \infty} sf(s) = \lim_{s \to \infty} L\{F'(t)\} + F(0^+).$$

We have $\lim_{s \to \infty} L\{F'(t)\} = 0$ by (a) so the first statement of part (c) follows.

From (2) it is clear that

$$\lim_{s \to 0^+} sf(s) = \lim_{s \to 0^+} L\{F'(t)\} + F(0^+) + \sum_{i=1}^{m} [F(t_i{}^+) - F(t_i{}^-)]$$

$$= \int_0^\infty \lim_{s \to 0^+} [e^{-st}F'(t)] \, dt + F(0^+) + \sum_{i=1}^{m} [F(t_i{}^+) - F(t_i{}^-)]$$

$$= \int_0^\infty F'(t) \, dt + F(0^+) + \sum_{i=1}^{m} [F(t_i{}^+) - F(t_i{}^-)]$$

$$= \lim_{t \to \infty} F(t) + \sum_{i=1}^{m} [F(t_i{}^+) - F(t_i{}^-)].$$

This concludes the proof of the theorem.

To illustrate part (c) of this theorem, we consider an example in which $f(s) = \dfrac{1}{s(s+k)}$ and $F(t) = \dfrac{1}{k}(1 - e^{-kt})$. Clearly $f(s) = L\{F(t)\}$ and since we know $F(t)$ explicitly in this example we could find the limit of $F(t)$ as t approaches either zero or infinity without using the results of Theorem XI. However, for purposes of illustration we compute

$$\lim_{s \to \infty} sf(s) = \lim_{s \to \infty} \frac{1}{s+k} = 0,$$

and

$$\lim_{s \to 0^+} sf(s) = \lim_{s \to 0^+} \frac{1}{s+k} = \frac{1}{k}, \qquad (k > 0).$$

We leave it to the student to verify that these two limits are $F(0^+)$ and $\lim_{t \to \infty} F(t)$, respectively.

EXERCISES 7

1. Check the results of Theorem XI, when applicable, on each of the following transform pairs:

(a) $f(s) = \dfrac{1}{s}$, $F(t) = 1$.

(b) $f(s) = \dfrac{1}{s+b}$, $F(t) = e^{-bt}$.

(c) $f(s) = \dfrac{s+b}{(s+b)^2 + k^2}$, $F(t) = e^{-bt} \cos kt$.

(d) $f(s) = \dfrac{s^2 - k^2}{(s^2 + k^2)^2}$, $F(t) = t \cos kt$.

(e) $f(s) = \dfrac{s^2 + k^2}{(s^2 - k^2)^2}$, $F(t) = t \cosh kt$.

2. Use the results of Theorem XI to find $\lim\limits_{t \to \infty} F(t)$ and $F(0^+)$ for the transforms:

(a) $f(s) = \dfrac{6}{(s+1)^2 + 4}$.

(c) $f(s) = \dfrac{8s + 16}{(s+2)^2 - 9}$.

(b) $f(s) = \dfrac{3}{(s+3)^3}$.

(d) $f(s) = \dfrac{s^2 - 9}{(s^2 + 9)^2}$.

3. Given $f(s) = \dfrac{2s + 5}{s^3 + 3s^2 + 3s + 1}$ find by Theorem XI and also directly:

(a) $\lim\limits_{t \to \infty} F(t)$.   (b) $F(0^+)$.   (c) $F'(0^+)$.

3

Unit Functions, Impulse Functions, and Periodic Functions

••

3.1 INTRODUCTION

We continue our development of basic properties of the Laplace transform. In this chapter, our principal concern is with the transforms of unit functions, impulse functions and periodic functions and with what we shall call "responses" to them.

3.2 THE UNIT STEP FUNCTION

One of the simplest discontinuous functions is the unit step function $\mathscr{U}(t - t_0)$ which is defined as follows:

$$(1) \qquad \mathscr{U}(t - t_0) = 0, \qquad (t < t_0),$$
$$= 1, \qquad (t \geq t_0).$$

It should be noted that $\mathscr{U}$ is a function of t and that t_0 plays the role of a parameter which indicates the point at which a unit step occurs. The graph of this function for $t_0 > 0$ is given in Fig. 8. It is clear that $\mathscr{U}(t - t_0)$ is a function of class T, and therefore possesses a Laplace transform, which we now compute.

$$(2) \qquad L\{\mathscr{U}(t - t_0)\} = \int_0^\infty \mathscr{U}(t - t_0)e^{-st}\,dt$$
$$= \int_0^{t_0} 0 \cdot e^{-st}\,dt + \int_{t_0}^\infty 1 \cdot e^{-st}\,dt$$
$$= \frac{e^{-st_0}}{s}, \qquad (s > 0).$$

In particular for $t_0 = 0$ we see that

(3) $$L\{\mathscr{U}(t)\} = \frac{1}{s}, \qquad (s > 0),$$

which is the result previously found in Chapter 1 when we computed $L\{1\}$.   A formula which may be obtained from equations (2) and (3) by use of the linearity property of the Laplace transform is

(4) $$L\{\mathscr{U}(t) - \mathscr{U}(t - t_0)\} = \frac{1}{s}(1 - e^{-st_0}), \qquad (s > 0).$$

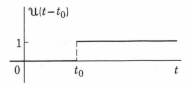

FIG. 8

This is useful when thought of as a formula for inverse transforms.†
In fact, an immediate generalization gives us inverse transforms of any linear combination of exponentials of the form e^{-as}/s.

Example 1.   For example, let us find

$$L^{-1}\left\{\frac{2}{s}(1 - 2e^{-s} + 2e^{-3s} - e^{-4s})\right\}.$$

From the linearity of the inverse transform, we have

$$L^{-1}\left\{\frac{2}{s}(1 - 2e^{-s} + 2e^{-3s} - e^{-4s})\right\}$$

$$= 2L^{-1}\left\{\frac{1}{s}\right\} - 4L^{-1}\left\{\frac{e^{-s}}{s}\right\} + 4L^{-1}\left\{\frac{e^{-3s}}{s}\right\} - 2L^{-1}\left\{\frac{e^{-4s}}{s}\right\}$$

$$= 2\mathscr{U}(t) - 4\mathscr{U}(t - 1) + 4\mathscr{U}(t - 3) - 2\mathscr{U}(t - 4),$$

where the last equality is obtained by repeated use of (2).

† Although functions such as $\dfrac{e^{-st_0}}{s}$ do not have unique inverse transforms, we may and shall usefully speak of their inverse transforms with the following understanding:

If $L\{F(t)\} = L\{G(t)\}$,   then $\int_0^t F(t)\,dt = \int_0^t G(t)\,dt$ for all $t \geq 0$.

See D. V. Widder, *The Laplace Transform* (Princeton, N.J., Princeton University Press, 1946), p. 63.

A more general use of the unit step function is illustrated in the following examples.

Example 2. Find $L\left\{\mathscr{U}\left(t - \dfrac{\pi}{2}\right) \sin t\right\}$.

Here,

$$L\left\{\mathscr{U}\left(t - \frac{\pi}{2}\right) \sin t\right\} = \int_0^\infty e^{-st}\mathscr{U}\left(t - \frac{\pi}{2}\right) \sin t \, dt$$

$$= \int_{\pi/2}^\infty e^{-st} \sin t \, dt$$

$$= -\frac{e^{-st}}{s^2 + 1} \left[\cos t + s \sin t\right]\Big|_{\pi/2}^\infty = e^{-(s\pi/2)}\frac{s}{s^2 + 1}.$$

Example 3. Find $L\{ [\mathscr{U}(t) - \mathscr{U}(t - 2)] (2 - t)\}$.

By definition,

$$f(s) = \int_0^\infty e^{-st}[\mathscr{U}(t) - \mathscr{U}(t - 2)](2 - t) \, dt.$$

Now in general the function $G(t) = \mathscr{U}(t - a) - \mathscr{U}(t - b)$ where $a < b$ has the functional values given by

$$\begin{aligned} G(t) &= 0, & (t < a), \\ &= 1, & (a \le t < b), \\ &= 0, & (t \ge b). \end{aligned}$$

Thus, since the function $[\mathscr{U}(t) - \mathscr{U}(t - 2)]$ is zero everywhere except $0 \le t < 2$, where it has the value 1, $f(s)$ may be written

$$f(s) = \int_0^2 e^{-st}(2 - t) \, dt$$

$$= -\frac{1}{s^2}(1 - e^{-2s}) + \frac{2}{s}.$$

In Example 2, the unit step function was used as a convenient tool to replace $\sin t$ by zero in $-\infty < t < \dfrac{\pi}{2}$; and in Example 3, the combination of unit functions gives a convenient method for writing a function which is zero everywhere except in $0 \leq t < 2$ where it has the values given by $2 - t$.   Thus if we are given a function which is expressed differently over different intervals, we may unify its expression by making use of the unit step functions.   To illustrate further, suppose we are given that in the range $t \geq 0$

$$F(t) = 1, \qquad (0 \leq t < 1),$$
$$= e^t, \qquad (1 \leq t < 2),$$
$$= 2, \qquad (t \geq 2),$$

and we wish to express $F(t)$ in a unified form.   To do this we note that

$$\mathscr{U}(t) - \mathscr{U}(t - 1) = 1, \qquad (0 \leq t < 1),$$
$$= 0, \qquad (\text{elsewhere}),$$
$$\mathscr{U}(t - 1) - \mathscr{U}(t - 2) = 1, \qquad (1 \leq t < 2),$$
$$= 0, \qquad (\text{elsewhere}),$$
$$\mathscr{U}(t - 2) = 1, \qquad (t \geq 2),$$
$$= 0, \qquad (t < 2).$$

Thus $F(t)$ may be written in the form

$$F(t) = [\mathscr{U}(t) - \mathscr{U}(t - 1)]1$$
$$+ [\mathscr{U}(t - 1) - \mathscr{U}(t - 2)]e^t + \mathscr{U}(t - 2)2, \qquad (t \geq 0).$$

EXERCISES I

Write each of the following functions for $t \geq 0$ in unified form in terms of the unit step functions and draw the graph of each:

1. $F(t) = 1, \qquad (0 \leq t < 1),$ 2. $F(t) = 0, \qquad \left(0 \leq t < \dfrac{\pi}{2}\right),$

   $\qquad = 4t - t^2, \; (1 \leq t < 2), \qquad \qquad = \sin t, \; \left(t \geq \dfrac{\pi}{2}\right).$

   $\qquad = 1, \qquad (t \geq 2).$

3. $F(t) = 1, \qquad (0 \leq t < 1),$

   $\qquad = e^{t-1}, \qquad (t \geq 1).$

4. $F(t) = t^2$, $(0 \leq t < 1)$,

       $= -(t^2 - 4t + 2)$, $(1 \leq t < 3)$,

       $= (t - 4)^2$, $(3 \leq t < 4)$,

       $= 0$, $(t \geq 4)$.

Find the Laplace transform of each of the following functions by performing the integration over the appropriate intervals:

5. $F(t) = 0$, $(0 \leq t < \pi)$,   **6.** $F(t) = 1$, $(0 \leq t < 1)$,

     $= \sin t$, $(\pi \leq t < 3\pi)$, $= e^t$, $(1 \leq t < 2)$,

     $= 0$, $(t \geq 3\pi)$. $= 2$, $(t \geq 2)$.

7. $F(t) = 1$, $(0 \leq t < 1)$,   **8.** $F(t) = 0$, $(0 \leq t < 1)$,

     $= 2 - t$, $(1 \leq t < 3)$, $= 4 - t^2$, $(1 \leq t < 3)$,

     $= -1$, $(t \geq 3)$. $= 0$, $(t \geq 3)$.

9. Use Theorem VI (Chapter 2, §2.3) to derive equation (2).

3.3 SPECIAL TRANSLATION THEOREM

We recall from analytic geometry that if $h > 0$, then the graph of $G(t - h)$ is the graph of $G(t)$ translated h units to the right. In particular if $G(t) = \mathcal{U}(t)F(t)$ then $G(t - h) = \mathcal{U}(t - h)F(t - h)$ and therefore (assuming $\mathcal{U}(t)F(t) = 0$ for $t < 0$)

(1) $G(t - h) = 0$, $(0 \leq t < h)$,

             $= F(t - h)$, $(h \leq t < \infty)$.

As an illustration consider $F(t) = 4 - 4t^2$. The graphs of $F(t)$, $G_1(t) = \mathcal{U}(t)F(t)$ and $G_2(t) = \mathcal{U}(t - 2)F(t - 2)$ are given by (a), (b), (c), respectively of Fig. 9. More generally, a function may be translated k units to the right and replaced by zero to the left of h simultaneously by the use of a product $\mathcal{U}(t - h)F(t - k)$. This is illustrated in the graph (d) of Fig. 9 in which $h = 1$, $k = 2$, and $F(t) = 4 - 4t^2$, $G_3(t) = \mathcal{U}(t - 1)F(t - 2)$.

The evaluation of Laplace transforms and their inverses is often facilitated by application of the following theorem.

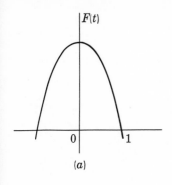

(a)

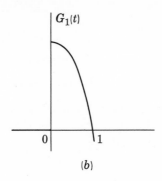

(b)

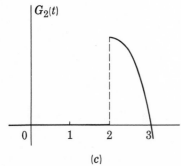

(c)

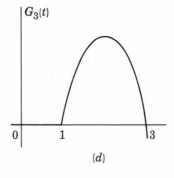

(d)

FIG. 9

Theorem XII.   *If $f(s) = L\{F(t)\}$, then*

(2) $$L\{\mathscr{U}(t - h)F(t - h)\} = e^{-hs}f(s), \qquad (h \geq 0).$$

Proof. $L\{\mathscr{U}(t - h)F(t - h)\} = \displaystyle\int_0^\infty e^{-st}\mathscr{U}(t - h)F(t - h)\,dt$

$$= \int_h^\infty e^{-st}F(t - h)\,dt.$$

If we set $t - h = T$, then

$$\int_h^\infty e^{-st}F(t - h)\,dt = \int_0^\infty e^{-s(T+h)}F(T)\,dT$$

$$= e^{-hs}\int_0^\infty e^{-sT}F(T)\,dT$$

$$= e^{-hs}f(s).$$

The next two examples illustrate Theorem XII.

Example 1. Given $F(t) = 4 - 4t^2$ find $L\{\mathcal{U}(t - 2)F(t)\}$.

In order to apply Theorem XII we must express $F(t)$ as a function of $(t - 2)$; that is (by synthetic division, or $F(t) = F(\overline{t - 2} + 2)$, etc.),

$$F(t) = -4(t - 2)^2 - 16(t - 2) - 12.$$

This form may be obtained either by inspection, as in this simple case, or by solving for the coefficients a, b, and c in the following identity:

$$4 - 4t^2 \equiv a(t - 2)^2 + b(t - 2) + c.$$

Applying (2) to $\mathcal{U}(t - 2)F(t)$ termwise, we get

$$L\{\mathcal{U}(t - 2)F(t)\} = -4L\{\mathcal{U}(t - 2)(t - 2)^2\} - 16L\{\mathcal{U}(t - 2)(t-2)\}$$

$$-12L\{\mathcal{U}(t - 2)\} = -4e^{-2s}\left(\frac{2}{s^3} + \frac{4}{s^2} + \frac{3}{s}\right).$$

Example 2. Find $L\{[\mathcal{U}(t - 1) - \mathcal{U}(t - 4)]4(1 - t)(t - 3)\}$.

In order to utilize Theorem XII we first write

$$[\mathcal{U}(t - 1) - \mathcal{U}(t - 4)]4(1 - t)(t - 3)$$
$$= \mathcal{U}(t - 1)4(1 - t)(t - 3) - \mathcal{U}(t - 4)4(1 - t)(t - 3),$$

and each term as follows:

$$\mathcal{U}(t - 1)4(1 - t)(t - 3) = \mathcal{U}(t - 1)[-4(t - 1)^2 + 8(t - 1)],$$
$$\mathcal{U}(t - 4)4(1 - t)(t - 3) = \mathcal{U}(t - 4)[-4(t - 4)^2 - 16(t - 4) - 12].$$

Therefore the desired transform is

$$L\{\mathcal{U}(t - 1)[-4(t - 1)^2 + 8(t - 1)]\}$$
$$- L\{\mathcal{U}(t - 4)[-4(t - 4)^2 - 16(t - 4) - 12]\}$$

$$= e^{-s}\left(\frac{-8}{s^3} + \frac{8}{s^2}\right) - e^{-4s}\left(\frac{-8}{s^3} - \frac{16}{s^2} - \frac{12}{s}\right).$$

Of course this transform could have been found by evaluating

$$\int_1^4 e^{-st}4(1 - t)(t - 3)\, dt$$

directly.   Example 1 may also be evaluated directly.

EXERCISES 2

1. Find $L\{\mathcal{U}(t-1)[(t-1)^3 + (t-1) + 6]\}$.

2. Find: (a) $L\{\mathcal{U}(t-2\pi)\cos(t-2\pi)\}$.

(b) $L\{\mathcal{U}(t-\pi)\sin t\}$.

3. Write out $L^{-1}\left\{\dfrac{1}{s^2}(1-e^{-s})\right\}$, using unit functions, and then sketch the inverse transform.

4. Write out $L^{-1}\left\{\dfrac{1}{s^2}(1-e^{-s})^2\right\}$, using unit functions, and then sketch the inverse transform.

5. Write out $L^{-1}\left\{\dfrac{1}{s^2}(1-e^{-s})^4\right\}$, using unit functions, and then sketch the inverse transform.

6. Show that

$$L^{-1}\left\{\frac{1}{s^3}(1-e^{-s})^3\right\} = \mathcal{U}(t)\frac{t^2}{2} - 3\mathcal{U}(t-1)\frac{(t-1)^2}{2}$$

$$+ 3\mathcal{U}(t-2)\frac{(t-2)^2}{2} - \mathcal{U}(t-3)\frac{(t-3)^2}{2}. \quad \text{Hence}$$

$$F(t) = \frac{t^2}{2}, \quad (0 \le t < 1),$$

$$= \frac{t^2}{2} - \tfrac{3}{2}(t-1)^2, \quad (1 \le t < 2),$$

$$= \frac{t^2}{2} - \tfrac{3}{2}(t-1)^2 + \tfrac{3}{2}(t-2)^2, \quad (2 \le t < 3),$$

$$= \frac{t^2}{2} - \tfrac{3}{2}(t-1)^2 + \tfrac{3}{2}(t-2)^2 - \frac{(t-3)^2}{2}, \quad (t \ge 3).$$

7. Find and sketch the inverse transforms of:

(a) $\dfrac{e^{-as}}{s^2+1}$, \qquad (b) $\dfrac{e^{-2s}}{s-1}$, \qquad (c) $\dfrac{se^{-3s}}{s^2-1}$.

3.4 TRANSFORMS OF FUNCTIONS FORMED BY GRAPHICAL ADDITION

We shall first illustrate the idea of *graphical addition* as it is used in finding the Laplace transforms of particular functions.

Example 1. Find $L\{G(t)\}$ if $G(t) = \begin{cases} \sin t, & (0 \le t < 2\pi), \\ 0, & (t \ge 2\pi). \end{cases}$

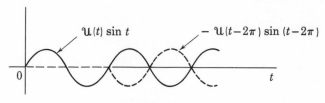

FIG. 10

The function $G(t)$ is clearly equal to the sum of the two functions $\mathcal{U}(t) \sin t$ and $-\mathcal{U}(t - 2\pi) \sin (t - 2\pi)$ whose graphs appear in Fig. 10, and hence $G(t)$ may be written

$$G(t) = \mathcal{U}(t) \sin t - \mathcal{U}(t - 2\pi) \sin (t - 2\pi).$$

Note that each term on the right is of the form $\mathcal{U}(t - a)F(t - a)$, and therefore Theorem XII may be applied to give

$$L\{G(t)\} = \frac{1}{s^2 + 1} - \frac{e^{-2\pi s}}{s^2 + 1} = \frac{1 - e^{-2\pi s}}{s^2 + 1}.$$

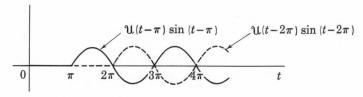

FIG. 11

Example 2. Find $L\{G(t)\}$ if

$$G(t) = 0, \qquad (0 \le t < \pi),$$
$$= -\sin t, \qquad (\pi \le t < 2\pi),$$
$$= 0, \qquad (t \ge 2\pi).$$

In this case we have, as illustrated in Fig. 11,

$$G(t) = \mathcal{U}(t - \pi) \sin (t - \pi) + \mathcal{U}(t - 2\pi) \sin (t - 2\pi).$$

Thus, by Theorem XII,

$$L\{G(t)\} = \frac{e^{-\pi s}}{s^2 + 1} + \frac{e^{-2\pi s}}{s^2 + 1} = \frac{e^{-\pi s}}{s^2 + 1} (1 + e^{-\pi s}).$$

Example 3.   Find the Laplace transform of the function $G(t)$ whose graph appears in Fig. 12.

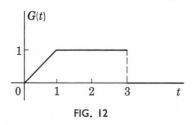

FIG. 12

The functions whose graphical sum is $G(t)$ are $\mathcal{U}(t)t$, $-\mathcal{U}(t - 1) \cdot (t - 1)$, and $-\mathcal{U}(t - 3)$.   Their graphs are given in Fig. 13.   Note

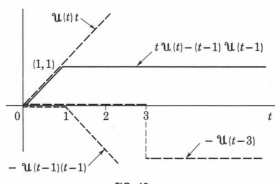

FIG. 13

that the sum $\mathcal{U}(t)t - \mathcal{U}(t - 1)(t - 1)$ is the solid line of Fig. 13. By adding $-\mathcal{U}(t - 3)$ to the sum we get

$$G(t) = \mathcal{U}(t)t - \mathcal{U}(t - 1)(t - 1) - \mathcal{U}(t - 3),$$

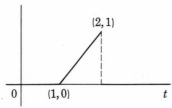

FIG. 14

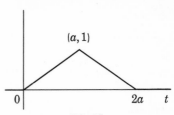

FIG. 15

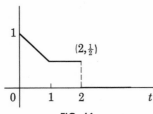

FIG. 16

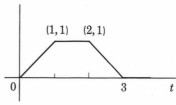

FIG. 17

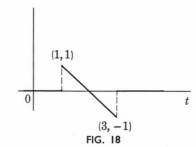

FIG. 18

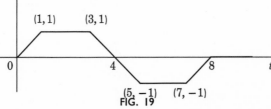

FIG. 19

which is the trapezoidal function of Fig. 12. Its transform is given immediately by Theorem XII as

$$L\{G(t)\} = \frac{1}{s^2} - \frac{e^{-s}}{s^2} - \frac{e^{-3s}}{s}.$$

EXERCISES 3

1. Express analytically the functions pictured in Figs. 14, 15 using unit functions. Find their transforms.

2. Find the transforms of the functions pictured in Figs. 16, 17, 18.

3. Graph and find the transform of

$$\mathscr{U}(t) \sin t - \mathscr{U}(t - 2\pi) \sin (t - 2\pi) - 2\mathscr{U}(t - 4\pi) \sin (t - 4\pi).$$

4. Taking $G(t) = \mathscr{U}(t)t - 2\mathscr{U}(t - a)(t - a) + \mathscr{U}(t - 2a)(t - 2a)$, graph and transform each of the following functions:

   (a) $G(t)$.   (b) $\mathscr{U}(t - 2a)G(t)$.   (c) $\mathscr{U}(t - 4a)G(t - 4a)$.

5. For $G(t)$ as in 4, find $L^{-1}\{sg(s)\}$ and graph it.

6. Express analytically using unit functions and then transform the function in Fig. 19.

3.5 TRANSFORMS OF PERIODIC FUNCTIONS

A function $F(t)$ is *periodic* of period T if, for all t, $F(t + T) = F(t)$. Transforms of periodic functions may be found by application of the following theorem.

Theorem XIII. *If $F(t)$ is periodic of period T (and has a transform) then*

(1) $$L\{F(t)\} = \frac{1}{1 - e^{-sT}} \int_0^T e^{-st} F(t)\, dt, \qquad (s > 0).$$

Proof. By definition, we have

(2) $$f(s) = \int_0^\infty e^{-st} F(t)\, dt = \int_0^T e^{-st} F(t)\, dt + \int_T^\infty e^{-st} F(t)\, dt.$$

In the last integral in (2) change to a new variable of integration by the substitution $t - T = y$. Then

$$\int_T^\infty e^{-st}F(t)\, dt = \int_0^\infty e^{-s(y+T)}F(y + T)\, dy$$

$$= \int_0^\infty e^{-s(y+T)}F(y)\, dy,$$

because $F(y + T) = F(y)$. Hence (2) becomes

(3) $\qquad f(s) = \int_0^T e^{-st}F(t)\, dt + e^{-sT}\int_0^\infty e^{-sy}F(y)\, dy$

$$= \int_0^T e^{-st}F(t)\, dt + e^{-sT}f(s).$$

Solving (3) for $f(s)$, we obtain

(4) $\qquad f(s) = \dfrac{1}{1 - e^{-sT}}\int_0^T e^{-st}F(t)\, dt.$

It is clear that since $F(t)$ is periodic, it is necessary to know the value of the function $F(t)$ only in the interval $0 \le t < T$ in order to compute its transform. However, it is sometimes useful to introduce a function $F_p(t)$ which equals $F(t)$ in the interval $0 \le t < T$ and is identically zero elsewhere. Such a function may be written by use of the unit functions in the form

(5) $\qquad F_p(t) = \mathscr{U}(t)F(t) - \mathscr{U}(t - T)F(t - T).$

Then $L\{F(t)\}$, for a periodic $F(t)$, may be written

(6) $\qquad L\{F(t)\} = \dfrac{1}{1 - e^{-sT}}f_p(s),$

where

(7) $\qquad f_p(s) = L\{F_p(t)\} = \int_0^\infty e^{-st}F_p(t)\, dt = \int_0^T e^{-st}F(t)\, dt.$

Example 1. For the "saw tooth" function in Fig. 20 we have

$$F_p(t) = \mathscr{U}(t)t - \mathscr{U}(t - 1)(t - 1) - \mathscr{U}(t - 1)$$

and

$$f_p(s) = \frac{1}{s^2} - \frac{1}{s^2}e^{-s} - \frac{1}{s}e^{-s} = \frac{1}{s^2}(1 - e^{-s}) - \frac{1}{s}e^{-s}.$$

Hence by (6) we have

(8) $f(s) = \dfrac{1}{s^2} - \dfrac{e^{-s}}{s(1 - e^{-s})} = L\{$saw tooth function of period $1\}.$

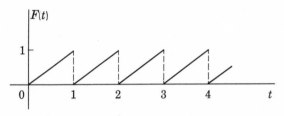

FIG. 20

Example 2. For the "square wave" function in Fig. 21, we have

$$F_p(t) = \mathscr{U}(t) - 2\mathscr{U}(t - a) + \mathscr{U}(t - 2a)$$

and

$$f_p(s) = \frac{1}{s}(1 - e^{-as})^2.$$

Hence

(9) $f(s) = \dfrac{(1 - e^{-as})^2}{s(1 - e^{-2as})} = \dfrac{1 - e^{-as}}{s(1 + e^{-as})} = \dfrac{1}{s}\tanh\dfrac{as}{2} = L\left\{\begin{matrix}\text{square wave}\\ \text{function of}\\ \text{period } 2a.\end{matrix}\right\}$

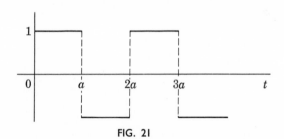

FIG. 21

Example 3. Let $F(t)$ be periodic of period $2a$ and let it coincide on the interval $0 \leq t < 2a$ with the function $G(t)$ in 4(a), Exercises 3. Then

(10) $f_p(s) = \dfrac{1}{s^2}\dfrac{(1 - e^{-as})^2}{1 - e^{-2as}} = \dfrac{1}{s^2}\tanh\dfrac{as}{2}\cdot$

EXERCISES 4

1.   Create periodic functions of period T and find their transforms as indicated:

(a) Use Fig. 17, taking $F_p(t)$ to coincide with the graph for $0 \leq t < 3$, $T = 3$.

(b) Same as (a), except the interval of coincidence is $0 \leq t < 4$ and $T = 4$.

(c) Use Fig. 18, taking $F_p(t)$ to coincide with the graph for $0 \leq t < 3$, $T = 3$.

(d) Use Fig. 19, taking $F_p(t)$ to coincide with the graph for $0 \leq t < 8$, $T = 8$.

2.   Find the transform of the following function (in the theory of alternating currents, called the half-wave rectification of the square wave):

$$F(t) = \begin{cases} 1, & (2na \leq t < (2n+1)a), \\ 0, & ((2n+1)a \leq t < (2n+2)a), \end{cases} \qquad (n = 0, 1, 2, \cdots).$$

3.   Find the transform of the function in Fig. 22 (called the half-wave rectification of $\sin \pi t$):

$$F(t) = \begin{cases} \sin \pi t, & (0 \leq t < 1), \\ 0, & (1 \leq t < 2), \\ F(t+2), & (t \geq 0). \end{cases}$$

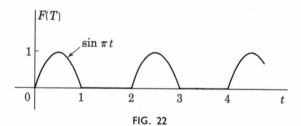

FIG. 22

4.   (a) If $F_p(t) = [\mathscr{U}(t-1) - \mathscr{U}(t-2)](1-t)(t-2)$, find $L\{F_p(t)\}$.

(b) If $F_p(t)$ is defined as in part (a), and if

$$F(t) = \begin{cases} 0, & (0 \leq t < 1), \\ F_p(t), & (1 \leq t < 2); \end{cases}$$

and $F(t+2) = F(t)$, $(t \geq 0)$, find $L\{F(t)\}$.

5. If $f_p(s) = \dfrac{1}{s}(1 + e^{-s} + e^{-2s} - e^{-3s} - e^{-4s} - e^{-5s})$, find $F_p(t)$ in terms of unit functions and graph it. Find the transform of the function

$$F(t) = F_p(t), \qquad (0 \le t < 7),$$
$$F(t + 7) = F(t), \qquad (t \ge 0).$$

6. Consider the wave form shown in Fig. 23, where

$$F_p(t) = \begin{cases} t^2/4, & (0 \le t < 1), \\ -(t^2 - 4t + 2)/4, & (1 \le t < 3), \\ (t - 4)^2/4, & (3 \le t < 4), \\ 0, & (t \ge 4). \end{cases}$$

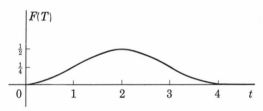

FIG. 23

Find $f_p(s)$ and the transform of the corresponding periodic function.

7. Find $f_p(s)$ if
$$F_p(t) = \mathscr{U}(t)t - 2\mathscr{U}(t - 1)(t - 1) + 2\mathscr{U}(t - 3)(t - 3)$$
$$- \mathscr{U}(t - 4)(t - 4).$$

8. Find the periodic functions whose transforms are:

(a) $$\left(\frac{1}{s} - \frac{1}{s^2} + \frac{e^{-s}}{s^2}\right)\bigg/(1 - e^{-2s}).$$

(b) $$\left(\frac{1}{s} + \frac{1}{s}e^{-s/2} - \frac{2}{s}e^{-s}\right)\bigg/(1 - e^{-3s}).$$

3.6 TRANSFORMS OF IMPULSE FUNCTIONS

Let us consider the problem of finding the transform of a force which produces a physical impulse, for instance, the blow of a hammer. As a mathematical idealization of such a force we may take any function $F(t)$, of the time t, which is zero except in a short interval $t_0 \leq t < t_1$. In particular, if K is a constant, the function which equals $\dfrac{K}{t_1 - t_0}$ in the interval $t_0 \leq t < t_1$ is easy to handle and gives satisfactory results for many applications. Such idealized functions are readily expressible in terms of the unit functions and are called *impulse functions*. In particular, for the impulse function $F(t)$ just described,

$$(1) \qquad F(t) = \frac{K}{t_1 - t_0} [\mathscr{U}(t - t_0) - \mathscr{U}(t - t_1)], \qquad (t_1 > t_0).$$

Notice that for $F(t)$ as in (1) we have

$$(2) \qquad \int_{-\infty}^{\infty} F(t)\, dt = K,$$

regardless of the values of t_0 and t_1, $(t_1 \neq t_0)$. The constant K is called the *strength* of the impulse function, and when $K = 1$ we refer to (1) as the *unit impulse function*.

In most cases it is convenient to think of an impulse function as acting at a certain instant, so we adopt as notation for (1),

$$F(t) = K\mathscr{I}(t - t_0, \varepsilon),$$

which means that the impulse function $F(t)$ is applied at time $t = t_0$, has a duration $\varepsilon > 0$ and the strength K. We therefore have for the impulse function (1) with $K = 1$, the *unit impulse function*

$$(3) \qquad \mathscr{I}(t - t_0, \varepsilon) = \frac{1}{\varepsilon}[\mathscr{U}(t - t_0) - \mathscr{U}(t - \overline{t_0 + \varepsilon})].$$

Since we know the transforms of the unit functions and since $\mathscr{I}$ is a linear combination of two of them we readily find that

$$(4) \qquad L\{\mathscr{I}(t - t_0, \varepsilon)\} = L\left\{\frac{1}{\varepsilon}[\mathscr{U}(t - t_0) - \mathscr{U}(t - \overline{t_0 + \varepsilon})]\right\}$$

$$= \frac{e^{-st_0}}{s\varepsilon}[1 - e^{-s\varepsilon}]$$

$$= e^{-st_0}\left[\frac{1 - e^{-s\varepsilon}}{s\varepsilon}\right].$$

Usually we think of an impulse function as being non-zero for a relatively short time.   If we write

$$(5) \quad \frac{1 - e^{-s\varepsilon}}{s\varepsilon} = \frac{1}{s\varepsilon}\left[1 - \left(1 - s\varepsilon + \frac{s^2\varepsilon^2}{2} - \cdots + (-1)^n \frac{(s\varepsilon)^n}{n!} + \cdots\right)\right]$$

$$= 1 - \frac{s\varepsilon}{2} + \frac{s^2\varepsilon^2}{3!} - \cdots + (-1)^n \frac{(s\varepsilon)^n}{(n+1)!} + \cdots,$$

we see that

$$(6) \qquad L\{\mathcal{I}(t - t_0, \varepsilon)\} = e^{-st_0}\left[1 - \frac{s\varepsilon}{2} + \frac{s^2\varepsilon^2}{3!} - \cdots\right].$$

Hence if ε is small, we have the approximation

$$(7) \qquad\qquad L\{\mathcal{I}(t - t_0, \varepsilon)\} \doteq e^{-st_0}.$$

In practice, it is usual to take this approximate value as the value of the transform of the impulse function $\mathcal{I}(t - t_0, \varepsilon)$.   We shall use the notation

$$(8) \qquad\qquad \mathcal{I}(t - t_0) = L^{-1}\{e^{-st_0}\}.$$

The property (7) is a special case of a more general one which we now illustrate.   Given any function $G(t)$ which is continuous in the range $t_0 \leq t \leq t_0 + \varepsilon$, let $G(t)$ be multiplied by $\mathcal{I}(t - t_0, \varepsilon)$ and the product integrated over the range $(-\infty, \infty)$.   Then the result is approximately equal to the value of $G(t_0)$.   To show this, we use a mean value theorem for integrals as follows:

$$(9) \quad \int_{-\infty}^{\infty} G(t)\mathcal{I}(t - t_0, \varepsilon)\, dt$$

$$= \frac{1}{\varepsilon}\int_{-\infty}^{\infty} G(t)[\mathcal{U}(t - t_0) - \mathcal{U}(t - \overline{t_0 + \varepsilon})]\, dt$$

$$= \frac{1}{\varepsilon}\int_{t_0}^{t_0+\varepsilon} G(t)\, dt$$

$$= \frac{1}{\varepsilon} \cdot \varepsilon \cdot G(t_0 + \theta\varepsilon)$$

$$= G(t_0 + \theta\varepsilon), \qquad \text{(for some } \theta, 0 < \theta < 1).$$

It is therefore clear that

$$(10) \qquad\qquad \int_{-\infty}^{\infty} G(t)\mathcal{I}(t - t_0, \varepsilon)\, dt \doteq G(t_0).$$

The result (7) is a special case of (10) with $G(t) = e^{-st}$ for $t \geq 0$, and $G(t) = 0$ for $t < 0$, $(t_0 \geq 0)$.

To illustrate the preceding ideas, let us consider a problem in which the driving force is the unit impulse function. For example, we might think of a simple pendulum (swinging in a short arc) being hit by a hammer at time† $t_0 > 0$. In this case the differential equation is

$$Y'' + k^2 Y = \mathscr{I}(t - t_0, \varepsilon), \qquad (t_0 > 0),$$

where $Y(t)$ is the displacement of the pendulum and the initial conditions are

$$Y(0) = Y'(0) = 0.$$

If we take the transform of both sides of the differential equation we get

$$(s^2 + k^2) y(s) = e^{-st_0} \left(1 - \frac{s\varepsilon}{2} + \frac{s^2 \varepsilon^2}{3!} - \cdots \right)$$

or

$$y(s) = \frac{e^{-st_0}}{s^2 + k^2} + \frac{e^{-st_0}}{s^2 + k^2} \left(-\frac{s\varepsilon}{2} + \frac{s^2 \varepsilon^2}{3!} - \cdots \right).$$

Upon taking the inverse transform we have

$$Y(t) = L^{-1} \left\{ \frac{e^{-st_0}}{s^2 + k^2} \right\} - \frac{\varepsilon}{2} L^{-1} \left\{ \frac{s e^{-st_0}}{s^2 + k^2} \right\}$$

$$+ \varepsilon^2 L^{-1} \left\{ \frac{e^{-st_0}}{s^2 + k^2} \left(\frac{s^2}{3!} - \frac{s^4 \varepsilon}{4!} + \cdots \right) \right\}$$

$$= \frac{\mathscr{U}(t - t_0)}{k} \sin k(t - t_0) - \frac{\varepsilon}{2} \mathscr{U}(t - t_0) \cos k(t - t_0)$$

$$+ \varepsilon^2 L^{-1} \left\{ \frac{e^{-st_0}}{s^2 + k^2} \left(\frac{s^2}{3!} - \frac{s^4 \varepsilon}{4!} + \cdots \right) \right\}.$$

Now if ε is a small quantity it is clear the first term in $Y(t)$ is dominant. But this is precisely the term which would have survived if in $y(s)$ we had used the approximate value of $L\{\mathscr{I}(t - t_0, \varepsilon)\}$ as given by (7).

---

† The impulse function is applied at $t = t_0 > 0$ in order that zero initial conditions can be satisfied. See §3.10 for further discussion of this point.

In the remainder of this chapter we shall assume that the necessary transforms and inverse transforms exist.   Thus the formal solution obtained in any particular case must be checked.

EXERCISES 5

Use the unit impulse function formally (as in equation (8)) whenever it occurs in this set.

1.   Show that $L^{-1}\left\{\dfrac{s-a}{s+a}\right\} = L^{-1}\left\{1 - \dfrac{2a}{s+a}\right\} = \mathscr{I}(t) - 2ae^{-at}$.

2.   Find: (a) $L^{-1}\left\{\dfrac{s}{s+a}\right\}$.

(b) $L^{-1}\left\{\dfrac{s^2}{s^2+1}\right\}$.

(c) $L^{-1}\left\{\dfrac{s^3}{s^3+1}\right\}$.

3.   Find: (a) $L\{\mathscr{I}(t-1) + \mathscr{I}(t-2) + \mathscr{I}(t-3) + \cdots\}$.

(b) $L\{\mathscr{I}(t-1) - \mathscr{I}(t-2) + \mathscr{I}(t-3) - \cdots\}$.

4.   Check the following:

(a) $L\left\{\displaystyle\int_0^t \mathscr{I}(t)\,dt\right\} = \dfrac{1}{s}$.

(b) $L^{-1}\left\{\dfrac{1}{s}\right\} = \displaystyle\int_0^t \mathscr{I}(T)\mathscr{U}(t-T)\,dT$.

5.   The triangular pulse of Fig. 24 has area 1.   Its transform is $\dfrac{1}{a^2s^2}\,[e^{-s(t_0-a)} - 2e^{-st_0} + e^{-s(t_0+a)}]$. Show that the limit of the transform as a approaches zero equals e^{-st_0}.

6.   Treat the parabolic pulse of Fig. 25 in a way similar to that of 5, to show that its transform approaches e^{-st_0} as $\varepsilon \to 0$.

7.   Check property (2) for the functions in 5 and 6.

8. Sketch the *unit doublet function* defined by

(11) $$\mathscr{D}(t - t_0, \varepsilon) = \frac{1}{\varepsilon}[\mathscr{I}(t - \overline{t_0 - \varepsilon}, \varepsilon) - \mathscr{I}(t - t_0, \varepsilon)].$$

Show that its transform is $\dfrac{e^{-st_0}}{s\varepsilon^2}(e^{s\varepsilon} + e^{-s\varepsilon} - 2)$, hence by analogy with (8), we have

(12) $$L\{\mathscr{D}(t - t_0)\} = se^{-st_0}.$$

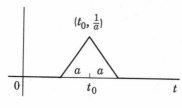

FIG. 24   FIG. 25

3.7 INDICIAL RESPONSE TO THE UNIT FUNCTION

Suppose a physical system is described by the differential equation and boundary conditions

(1) $$\begin{cases} A Y''(t) + B Y'(t) + C Y(t) = F(t), \\ Y(0) = Y'(0) = 0, \end{cases}$$

where A, B, C are constants and $F(t)$ is a known function, called the *driving function*. The solution $Y(t)$ is called the *response function*. When $F(t) = \mathscr{U}(t)$ in (1), the solution $Y(t)$ is called the *indicial response*, $Y_1(t)$, *to the unit function*. Thus

$$y_1(s) = L\{Y_1(t)\} = \frac{1}{s(As^2 + Bs + C)},$$

so

(2) $$Y_1(t) = L^{-1}\{y_1(s)\}.$$

Example 1. If, in (1), we take $A = 1$, $B = 0$, $C = \omega^2 > 0$, $F(t) = \mathscr{U}(t)$, then

$$Y_1(t) = L^{-1}\left\{\frac{1}{s(s^2 + \omega^2)}\right\} = \frac{1}{\omega^2}(1 - \cos \omega t).$$

Example 2. The differential system for the current I in an R–L series circuit† with unit voltage applied at $t = 0$ is

$$L\frac{dI}{dt} + RI = \mathscr{U}(t), \qquad I(0) = 0,$$

where R = resistance, L = inductance, both constant.

Hence

$$i_1(s) = \frac{1}{Ls\left(s + \dfrac{R}{L}\right)},$$

and

$$I_1(t) = L^{-1}\{i_1(s)\} = \frac{1}{R}\left(1 - e^{-(Rt/L)}\right).$$

3.8 RESPONSE TO A GENERAL DRIVING FUNCTION

The terminology of §3.7 is applied to the more general differential equation with zero initial conditions:

$$(1) \quad \begin{cases} \Phi(D)Y(t) = F(t), \; \Phi(D) = A_0 D^n + A_1 D^{n-1} + \cdots + A_n, \\ Y(0) = Y'(0) = \cdots = Y^{(n-1)}(0) = 0, \end{cases}$$

where A_i is a constant and $D^k Y(t)$ denotes the kth derivative of $Y(t)$. The formal solution of (1) is

$$(2) \qquad Y(t) = L^{-1}\{y(s)\} = L^{-1}\left\{\frac{f(s)}{\Phi(s)}\right\}.$$

The indicial response in this general case is

$$(3) \qquad Y_1(t) = L^{-1}\{y_1(s)\} = L^{-1}\left\{\frac{1}{s\Phi(s)}\right\}.$$

The function $\Phi(s)$ is called the *characteristic function* of (1).

3.9 SUPERPOSITION THEOREM FOR RESPONSE TO THE UNIT FUNCTION

The solution $Y(t)$ of (2) is related to the indicial response $Y_1(t)$ of (3) §3.8, as follows:

† See Appendix IV.

Theorem XIV.   *For $Y(t)$, $Y_1(t)$, and $F(t)$ as given in §3.8, we have*

(1)
$$Y(t) = F(0) Y_1(t) + \int_0^t F'(T) Y_1(t - T) \, dT$$
$$= F(0) Y_1(t) + \int_0^t F'(t - T) Y_1(T) \, dT.$$

Proof.   By (2) and (3), §3.8, we have

$$y(s) = \frac{f(s)}{\Phi(s)} \quad \text{and} \quad y_1(s) = \frac{1}{s\Phi(s)} \cdot$$

Hence, under strong enough assumptions on $F(t)$, we obtain

$$y(s) = y_1(s)sf(s) = y_1(s)[L\{F'(t)\} + F(0)]$$
$$= F(0)y_1(s) + y_1(s)L\{F'(t)\}$$
$$= F(0)L\{Y_1(t)\} + L\{Y_1(t) * F'(t)\},$$

from which the theorem follows (by the Convolution Theorem, Theorem VII, §2.4).

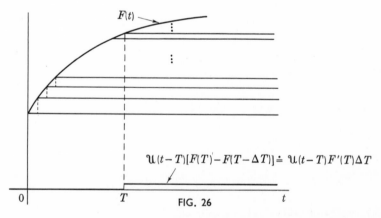

$$\mathfrak{U}(t-T)[F(T)-F(T-\Delta T)] \doteq \mathfrak{U}(t-T)F'(T)\Delta T$$

0   T   FIG. 26   t

This result is made plausible by considering the response $Y(t)$ at any time t as the limit of the sum of all individual responses due to preceding step functions $\mathfrak{U}(t - T)F'(T) \, \Delta T$.   The response to the first unit function $\mathfrak{U}(t)$ is $F(0) Y_1(t)$.   The response to the nth step is $F'(T) \, \Delta T \, Y_1(t - n \, \Delta T)$.   See Fig. 26, where $T = n\Delta T$.

3.10 INDICIAL RESPONSE TO THE UNIT IMPULSE FUNCTION

If in equations (1), §3.8, we take $F(t) = \mathscr{I}(t)$, the function

$$(1) \qquad Y_2(t) = L^{-1}\{y_2(s)\} = L^{-1}\left\{\frac{1}{\Phi(s)}\right\}$$

is the result of the formal application of the Laplace transform technique. The function $Y_2(t)$ is called the *indicial response to the unit impulse function*. It is interesting to note that $L^{-1}\left\{\dfrac{1}{\Phi(s)}\right\}$ is the actual solution of the differential system **given by (1),** §3.8, if $Y^{(n-1)}(0)$ is taken to be unity instead of zero and $F(t)$ is identically zero instead of $\mathscr{I}(t)$. As the following example shows, $Y_2(t)$ does not satisfy the initial conditions. However it is analogous to the response to the unit function and, as we shall see in §3.11, again enables us to express the solution of the problem in which $F(t)$ is a general driving function of class T in terms of the convolution of $F(t)$ and $Y_2(t)$.

Example. Find $Y_2(t)$ for the differential system

$$\begin{cases} (D^2 + 1)^2 Y(t) = \mathscr{I}(t), \\ Y(0) = Y'(0) = Y''(0) = Y'''(0) = 0. \end{cases}$$

Here

$$y_2(s) = \frac{1}{(s^2 + 1)^2},$$

and by Example 3, §2.4, we have

$$(2) \qquad Y_2(t) = \tfrac{1}{2}(\sin t - t \cos t).$$

The reader may verify that $Y_2'''(0) = 1$ if $Y_2'''(0)$ is computed directly from (2).

3.11 SUPERPOSITION THEOREM FOR THE RESPONSE TO THE UNIT IMPULSE FUNCTION

Since from (2), §3.8 and (1), §3.10 we have

$$y(s) = \frac{f(s)}{\Phi(s)} \quad \text{and} \quad y_2(s) = \frac{1}{\Phi(s)},$$

we obtain the following analogy to Theorem XIV:

Theorem XV.

(1)
$$Y(t) = \int_0^t F(T)\, Y_2(t-T)\, dT$$

$$= \int_0^t F(t-T)\, Y_2(T)\, dT.$$

Note that the formal application of Theorem XV does not call for $F'(t)$.

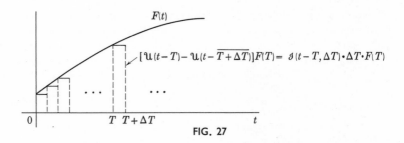

FIG. 27

The result of Theorem XV is made plausible by considering the response $Y_2(t-T)$ due to the unit impulse function applied at T. If $F(T)$ is regarded as the "continuous" system of impulses shown in Fig. 27, then the response $Y(t)$ at any time t is the sum of all the elementary responses started previous to t.

Example.   Use Theorem XV and the Example of §3.10 to solve

$$\begin{cases} (D^2 + 1)^2 Y(t) = \sin t, \\ Y(0) = Y'(0) = Y''(0) = Y'''(0) = 0. \end{cases}$$

Using (1), §3.11 and (2), §3.10 we have

$$Y(t) = \tfrac{1}{2}\int_0^t \sin(t-T) \cdot (\sin T - T\cos T)\, dT$$

$$= \tfrac{1}{8}[(3 - t^2)\sin t - 3t\cos t].$$

EXERCISES 6

1. Find the indicial response to the unit function and to the unit impulse function if, in (1), §3.8 $\Phi(D)$ is taken to be:

(a) $D^2 + 5D + 6$.

(b) $D^2 - 2D + 2$.

2. Show that equation (1), §3.9 yields

$$Y(t) = \int_0^t F(T) Y_1'(t - T) \, dT = \int_0^t F(t - T) Y_1'(T) \, dT.$$

3.12 SYSTEMS WITH ONE DEGREE OF FREEDOM

The mechanical system of Fig. 28 and the electrical system† of

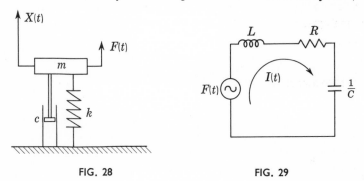

FIG. 28   FIG. 29

Fig. 29 are described by a second order differential of the form

(1) $X''(t) + 2aX'(t) + \gamma^2 X(t) = F(t),$

where $a \geq 0$ and $\gamma > 0$. We shall solve this equation subject to the initial conditions

(2) $X(0) = X_0, \qquad X'(0) = X_0',$

where the constants X_0, X_0' are not necessarily zero. Taking the

† See Appendix IV for the definitions and laws relevant to electrical circuits.

transform of both sides of (1) and making use of conditions (2), we get

$$x(s) = \frac{f(s) + X_0(s + 2a) + X_0{}'}{s^2 + 2as + \gamma^2}$$

(3)

$$= \frac{X_0(s + 2a) + X_0{}' + f(s)}{(s + a)^2 + \gamma^2 - a^2}.$$

If $\gamma > a$, then $b^2 = \gamma^2 - a^2$ is a real positive number and the denominator of (3) has imaginary zeros, namely $-a + ib$ and $-a - ib$. In this case

$$(4) \quad L^{-1}\left\{\frac{X_0(s + 2a)}{(s + a)^2 + b^2}\right\} = L^{-1}\left\{\frac{X_0(s + a)}{(s + a)^2 + b^2}\right\} + L^{-1}\left\{\frac{X_0 a}{(s + a)^2 + b^2}\right\}$$

$$= X_0 e^{-at} \cos bt + \frac{X_0 a}{b} e^{-at} \sin bt,$$

$$(5) \quad L^{-1}\left\{\frac{X_0{}'}{(s + a)^2 + b^2}\right\} = \frac{X_0{}'}{b} e^{-at} \sin bt,$$

and

$$(6) \quad L^{-1}\left\{\frac{f(s)}{(s + a)^2 + b^2}\right\} = F(t) * \frac{e^{-at} \sin bt}{b}$$

$$= \frac{1}{b} \int_0^t F(T) e^{-a(t - T)} \sin b(t - T) \, dT.$$

The general solution of equation (1) with boundary conditions (2) and with $\gamma > a$ is therefore

$$(7) \quad X(t) = \frac{X_0 e^{-at}}{b} (a \sin bt + b \cos bt) + \frac{X_0{}'}{b} e^{-at} \sin bt$$

$$+ \frac{1}{b} \int_0^t F(T) e^{-a(t - T)} \sin b(t - T) \, dT.$$

Of the three terms on the right-hand side of (7), the second is the response to $X_0{}'\mathscr{I}(t)$, while the third term is precisely the integral given by (1), §3.11 of Theorem XV.

If $a > 0$, we can see from the exponential factor e^{-at} in the solution (7) that the physical system characterized by (1) and (2) is inherently a *damped system*, that is, it absorbs energy received from its driving source. This energy is not recovered, since it is dissipated in heat or friction losses. Thus the system will damp out unless enough energy is supplied by the driving function to overcome these natural losses and still have the excess energy to actuate the system and produce a sustained or *steady state* response.

EXERCISES 7

1. Find the relation between the first term of equation (7) and the response to the unit function.

2. Solve equation (1) if $F(t) = \mathscr{U}(t)$, $X_0 = X_0' = 0$, $a = 3$, $\gamma = 5$.

3. Show that equation (4) may be written

$$L^{-1}\left\{\frac{X_0(s + 2a)}{(s + a)^2 + b^2}\right\} = \frac{1}{b} X_0 e^{-at} A \cos (bt - \theta),$$

where $A^2 = b^2 + a^2$ and $\tan \theta = \dfrac{a}{b}$.

4. Employ equation (7) to solve $(D^2 + 6D + 25)X(t) = 6$, with $X_0 = 1$, $X_0' = 0$. Write the solution for $X(t)$ with two terms, one containing the factor e^{-3t} and one showing the steady state.

5. Solve $(D^2 + 2D + 170)X(t) = 2$, with $X_0 = 1$, $X_0' = 1$.

6. Solve $(D^2 + 2D + 2)X(t) = 0$, with:

(a) $X_0 = 1$, $X_0' = 10$.

(b) $X_0 = 1$, $X(1) = 2$.

(c) $X_0' = 0$, $X'\left(\dfrac{\pi}{2}\right) = 1$.

7. Solve equation (1) if $a = 0$, $F(t) = F_0 \sin \gamma t$, $X_0 = X_0' = 0$. Sketch the solution.

8. Solve equation (1) if $a = 3$, $\gamma = 5$, $F(t) = \mathscr{I}(t - 1)$, and $X_0 = X_0' = 0$. First do this by direct use of partial fractions, and then check your result by substitution in (7).

4

Applications to Ordinary Differential Equations

••

4.1 INTRODUCTION

We now apply the Laplace Transform technique to some typical physical problems with one or two degrees of freedom. These problems will lead to ordinary differential equations or systems of ordinary differential equations with appropriate boundary conditions. The driving functions involved may be discontinuous and include both periodic and non-periodic types.

4.2 SPECIAL PERIODIC DRIVING FUNCTION

In §3.12 we considered the differential equation

(1) $\qquad X''(t) + 2aX'(t) + \gamma^2 X(t) = F(t), \qquad (a \geq 0, \gamma > 0).$

The general solution of equation (1) can be written as the sum of two kinds of functions

$$X(t) = C(t) + P(t).$$

The function $C(t)$, which is called the *complementary function* of equation (1), is the general solution of the homogeneous equation formed from (1) when $F(t)$ is replaced by 0. $P(t)$ is a *particular integral*, that is, it is any particular solution of the equation (1) itself. In general, $C(t)$ and $P(t)$ are sums of terms of two essentially different types. The first type is usually contained in the complementary function. It has an exponential decay factor (that is, a factor of the form e^{-at}, $a > 0$) and therefore vanishes as $t \to \infty$.

Hence it is called a *transient* term. The total transient involves two arbitrary constants which are determined by the initial conditions. The second type of term that may occur in the general solution does not decay with time but continues indefinitely in some pattern and for this reason is called a *steady state* term. It is usually given by the particular integral. If $a = 0$ in equation (1), the complementary function may contain a periodic term which has no decay factor associated with it and this term should be included in the steady state solution. However, since this cannot actually occur physically (that is, there is always some resistance present even though it may be small), it is a common engineering practice to assume that steady state terms are found only in the particular integral.

In the important case in which the driving function is given by

$$(2) \qquad F(t) = F_0 e^{i\omega t}, \qquad F_0 \text{ a constant}, \qquad i = \sqrt{-1},$$

the steady state solution will contain a term with the same frequency ω as contained in the driving function but lagging behind the latter. Let us substitute (2) into (1) and consider the steady state response to zero initial conditions, that is, $X_0 = X_0' = 0$. Taking the transform of (1) with $F(t)$ as in (2), we get

$$(3) \qquad x(s) = \frac{F_0}{(s - i\omega)(s^2 + 2as + \gamma^2)}$$

$$= \frac{F_0}{[b^2 + (a + i\omega)^2](s - i\omega)}$$

$$+ \frac{A_1(s + a) + A_2}{(s + a)^2 + b^2}, \qquad (b^2 = \gamma^2 - a^2).$$

Since the last term will lead to a transient containing e^{-at} as a factor, to find the steady state response we consider the inverse of only the first term, namely,

$$(4) \quad L^{-1}\left\{ \frac{F_0}{[b^2 + (a + i\omega)^2](s - i\omega)} \right\} = \frac{F_0 e^{i\omega t}}{b^2 + (a + i\omega)^2}$$

$$= \frac{F_0[\cos(\omega t - \theta) + i\sin(\omega t - \theta)]}{[4a^2\omega^2 + (\gamma^2 - \omega^2)^2]^{1/2}},$$

where $\tan \theta = 2a\omega/(\gamma^2 - \omega^2)$. Equation (4) is the complex steady state solution of equation (1) with driving function (2) and zero initial conditions. The real and imaginary coefficients of this solution are in fact the solutions to the corresponding real problems in which the driving functions are $F_0 \cos \omega t$ and $F_0 \sin \omega t$, respectively.

4.3 DISCONTINUOUS DRIVING FUNCTIONS†

In this section we shall solve three examples in which $F(t)$ is discontinuous.

Example 1. In the one-loop circuit of Fig. 29, §3.12, take $L = 0$, $F(t) = F_0[\mathcal{U}(t - t_1) - \mathcal{U}(t - t_2)]$, $t_2 > t_1$, F_0 constant, and initial charge $Q(0) = Q_0$ arbitrary. Find the current $I(t)$.

Under these conditions, the differential equation‡ of the circuit is

$$(1) \qquad RQ'(t) + \frac{1}{C}\, Q(t) = F_0 \mathcal{U}(t - t_1) - F_0 \mathcal{U}(t - t_2),$$

and the transform of the solution is

$$(2) \qquad q(s) = \frac{Q_0}{s + a} + \frac{F_0/R}{s(s + a)}\, (e^{-st_1} - e^{-st_2}), \qquad a = 1/RC.$$

Thus

$$(3) \qquad i(s) = L\{Q'(t)\} = sq(s) - Q_0$$

$$= \frac{sQ_0}{s + a} - Q_0 + \frac{F_0/R}{s + a}\, (e^{-st_1} - e^{-st_2}).$$

The current $I(t) = L^{-1}\{i(s)\}$ is given by

$$(4) \qquad I(t) = -aQ_0 e^{-at} + (F_0/R)[\mathcal{U}(t - t_1)e^{-a(t - t_1)}$$

$$-\, \mathcal{U}(t - t_2)e^{-a(t - t_2)}]$$

$$= -aQ_0 e^{-at}, \qquad (0 \le t < t_1),$$

$$= -aQ_0 e^{-at} + (F_0/R)e^{-a(t - t_1)}, \qquad (t_1 \le t < t_2),$$

$$= -aQ_0 e^{-at} + (F_0/R)[e^{-a(t - t_1)} - e^{-a(t - t_2)}], \qquad (t \ge t_2).$$

† For the existence and uniqueness of a solution in the case of a class T function $F(t)$, see E. A. Coddington and N. Levinson, *Theory of Differential Equations* (New York, McGraw-Hill, 1955), pp. 97–98.

‡ By the theory of such equations, there exists a unique and continuous solution for the charge $Q(t)$.

Note the lack of any steady state terms in this solution.   The charge $Q(t)$ may be obtained by finding the inverse transform of $q(s)$ as given in (2).

Example 2.   Fig. 30 shows a mass m connected to supports by means of springs having a total effective spring constant k.   The mass slides on the smooth surface experiencing a square wave driving function of

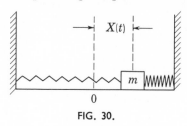

FIG. 30.

magnitude $\pm A$ acting as pictured in Fig. 31.   If we set $\omega^2 = k/m$ and $G(t) = \dfrac{F(t)}{m}$, then the equation of motion becomes

(5) $$X'' + \omega^2 X = G(t).$$

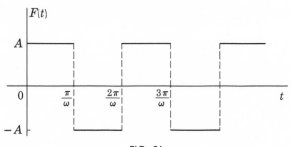

FIG. 31

Suppose that the mass is initially at rest ($X'(0) = 0$) at the point $X = X_0 > 0$ and that $\omega^2 X_0$ exceeds A/m sufficiently to guarantee motion after release at $t = 0$.   Solve for $X(t)$.

Equation (5) can be rewritten in terms of unit functions as follows:

(6) $$X'' + \omega^2 X = \frac{A}{m}\left[\mathcal{U}(t) - 2\mathcal{U}\left(t - \frac{\pi}{\omega}\right) + 2\mathcal{U}\left(t - \frac{2\pi}{\omega}\right) - \cdots\right].$$

The transform of (6) is†

(7) $s^2 x(s) - s X_0 + \omega^2 x(s)$

$$= \frac{A}{ms} [1 - 2e^{-sT} + 2e^{-2sT} - 2e^{-3sT} + \cdots],$$

where $T = \dfrac{\pi}{\omega}$, the *half-period*.   Thus we have

(8) $x(s) = \dfrac{s X_0}{s^2 + \omega^2} + \dfrac{A}{ms(s^2 + \omega^2)} [1 - 2e^{-sT} + \cdots],$

hence

$$X(t) = X_0 \cos \omega t + \frac{A}{m\omega^2} (1 - \cos \omega t), \qquad (0 \leq t < T),$$

$$= X_0 \cos \omega t + \frac{A}{m\omega^2} (1 - \cos \omega t)$$

$$- \frac{2A}{m\omega^2} [1 - \cos \omega(t - T)], \quad (T \leq t < 2T),$$

$$= X_0 \cos \omega t + \frac{A}{m\omega^2} (1 - \cos \omega t)$$

$$- \frac{2A}{m\omega^2} [1 - \cos \omega(t - T)]$$

$$+ \frac{2A}{m\omega^2} [1 - \cos \omega(t - 2T)], \; (2T \leq t < 3T),$$

$$\vdots$$

Thus,

(9) $X(t) = X_0 \cos \omega t + \dfrac{A}{m\omega^2} (1 - \cos \omega t)$

$$+ \frac{2A}{m\omega^2} \sum_{p=1}^{n} (-1)^p (1 - \cos \omega(t - pT))$$

$$= \left(X_0 - (2n + 1) \frac{A}{m\omega^2} \right) \cos \omega t$$

$$\pm \frac{A}{m\omega^2}, \qquad (nT \leq t < (n + 1)T).$$

† The transform is more convenient in the form (7) for this problem than in the form given by Theorem XIII, §3.5.   See Example 2, §3.5.

A sketch of this solution for the first few periods for particular values of X_0, $A/m\omega^2$ is shown in Fig. 32. (The straight line segment in this sketch may or may not occur in general, depending on whether X_0 is an odd multiple of $A/m\omega^2$ or not.) It is interesting to observe that the amplitude of the motion is ultimately increasing as time progresses. An explanation of this behavior may be obtained

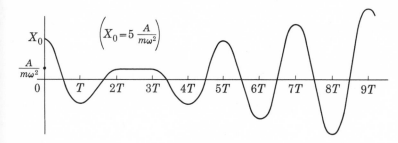

FIG. 32

by comparing equation (6) with the general equation (1), §4.2. The fact that there is no first derivative term in (6) is equivalent to setting $a = 0$ in (1), §4.2. Physically, this means that there is no friction in the system.   Now the homogeneous equation associated with (6), namely,

$$X'' + \omega^2 X = 0$$

has a periodic solution with frequency $\dfrac{\omega}{2\pi}$, which is called the *undamped natural frequency* of the system.   The increase in amplitude of the solution of (6) as given by (9) and illustrated in Fig. 32 results from the fact that the driving force has the same frequency as the natural frequency of the system so that the driving force reinforces the natural frequency and produces a condition known as *resonance*.

Example 3. Fig. 33 represents a driving function, applied to a mass m on a frictionless horizontal plane, which we interpret as a series of impulsive blows of "strength" A acting on the mass m at times a, $2a$, $3a$, $\cdots$. Find the velocity at any time under the assumption that the initial velocity is A/m.

The equation of motion is

$$(10) \qquad m \frac{dV}{dt} = A[\mathscr{I}(t-a) + \mathscr{I}(t-2a) + \cdots],$$

and its transform is

$$(11) \qquad sv(s) = \frac{A}{m}[1 + e^{-sa} + e^{-2sa} + \cdots].$$

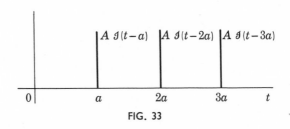

FIG. 33

Hence, upon inverting $v(s)$ we obtain the velocity $V(t)$:

$$(12) \qquad V(t) = \frac{A}{m}[\mathscr{U}(t) + \mathscr{U}(t-a) + \mathscr{U}(t-2a) + \cdots].$$

We picture this "staircase function" in Fig. 34 and note that†

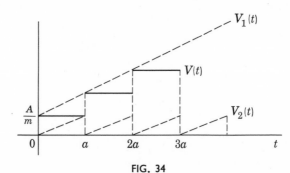

FIG. 34

$$V(t) = V_1(t) - V_2(t),$$

where

$$V_1(t) = \frac{At}{ma} + \frac{A}{m} \quad \text{and} \quad V_2(t) = [\text{saw tooth function}].$$

† A continuous solution $V(t)$ should not be expected in this case.

For the reader acquainted with Fourier series, we remark that

$$(13) \qquad V_2(t) = \frac{A}{m}\left[\frac{1}{2} - \frac{1}{\pi}\sum_{n=1}^{\infty}\frac{1}{n}\sin\frac{2n\pi t}{a}\right],$$

and

$$(14) \qquad V(t) = \frac{A}{m}\left[\frac{t}{a} + \frac{1}{2} + \frac{1}{\pi}\sum_{n=1}^{\infty}\frac{1}{n}\sin\frac{2n\pi t}{a}\right]$$

are the Fourier series representations of these functions.

EXERCISES I

1. Verify equation (4), §4.2. Discuss the case $\gamma^2 = \omega^2$.

2. Find $Q(t)$ from (2), §4.3, and show it is continuous. Sketch the charge $Q(t)$ and the current $I(t)$.

3. Suppose the circuit of Fig. 29 has $R = 0$. If $F(t)$ is given by $E_0t[\mathscr{U}(t) - \mathscr{U}(t - t_0)]$ and $Q(0) = I(0) = 0$, E_0 a constant, find the current $I(t)$.

4. Solve 3 if $F(t) = E_0 \sin \omega t$. Discuss the case $\omega^2 = 1/LC$.

5. In an RLC series circuit, the impressed voltage is given by $E_1 \cos \omega_1 t + E_2 \cos \omega_2 t$. Find the steady state solution.

6. If $X(0) = X'(0) = 0$, solve $\left(D^2 + \dfrac{\pi^2}{T^2}\right)X(t) = F(t)$, where $F(t)$ is the square wave function of unit amplitude and period $2T$.

7. Solve the following equation for the current $I(t)$:

$$RI(t) + \frac{1}{C}\int_0^t I(t)\, dt = E_0|\sin \omega t|.$$

8. Solve 7 with zero initial conditions when the impressed voltage is the periodic quarter cosine wave shown in Fig. 35.

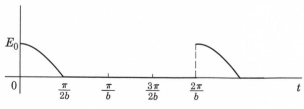

FIG. 35

9. Integrate equation (12), §4.3 from $t = 0$ to $t = 4a$, to find how far the mass has moved during this length of time. Check your result by integrating equation (14).

4.4 SYSTEMS WITH TWO DEGREES OF FREEDOM

Example 1. In Figs. 36 and 37 two analogous systems are shown.

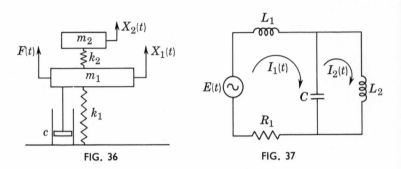

FIG. 36   FIG. 37

The corresponding systems of equations are

(1)
$$\begin{cases} m_1 X_1'' + c X_1' + k_1 X_1 + k_2(X_1 - X_2) = F(t), \\ m_2 X_2'' + k_2(X_2 - X_1) = 0. \end{cases}$$

(2)
$$\begin{cases} L_1 I_1' + R_1 I_1 + \dfrac{1}{C} \int_0^t (I_1 - I_2)\, dt = E(t), \\ L_2 I_2' + \dfrac{1}{C} \int_0^t (I_2 - I_1)\, dt = 0. \end{cases}$$

If in the second system we set $I_1 = Q_1'$ and $I_2 = Q_2'$, then the two systems of equations take the same form and the analogous elements are

displacement	X	charge	Q
mass	m	inductance	L
friction	c	resistance	R
spring modulus	k	elastance	$1/C$
force	$F(t)$	voltage	$E(t)$
velocity	$V = X'$	current	$I = Q'$.

We shall study the system (1) with $F(t) = F_0 \sin \omega t$ and initial conditions $X_1(0) = X_2(0) = X_1'(0) = X_2'(0) = 0$.   The transformed equations are

(3) $\begin{cases} x_1(s)(m_1 s^2 + cs + k_1 + k_2) - k_2 x_2(s) = F_0 \omega/(s^2 + \omega^2), \\ -k_2 x_1(s) + x_2(s)(m_2 s^2 + k_2) = 0. \end{cases}$

Elimination of $x_2(s)$ from these two equations gives

(4) $x_1(s) = \dfrac{F_0 \omega (m_2 s^2 + k_2)}{[(m_1 s^2 + cs + k_1 + k_2)(m_2 s^2 + k_2) - k_2^2][s^2 + \omega^2]}$.

The motion of mass m_1 is given by the inverse of (4).   In general, a steady state will exist, for if the expression for $x_1(s)$ is separated into partial fractions, there is one fraction which has the denominator $s^2 + \omega^2$ and hence one term of the solution is sinusoidal and not damped out as t increases indefinitely.   For the second mass m_2 we define its natural frequency as $\omega_2 = \sqrt{k_2/m_2}$.   If the design of this spring and mass is such that its natural frequency is the same as the frequency of the exciting function $F(t) = F_0 \sin \omega t$, that is

$$k_2/m_2 = \omega^2,$$

then (4) becomes

$$x_1(s) = m_2 F_0 \omega / \Delta(s),$$

where the characteristic transform $\Delta(s)$ is the first factor in the denominator of (4).   In this case, $x_1(s)$ cannot contain a steady state term because the denominator $\Delta(s)$ has no zeros which are purely imaginary.   In fact it can be shown† that all roots of $\Delta(s) = 0$ have negative real parts, hence $X_1(t)$ contains exponential decaying terms, causing the mass m_1 to have its motion damped out.   This feature of the system is typical of a *vibration absorber*.   Here, the second mass system is the absorber and its motion is given by the inverse of

$$x_2(s) = \frac{k_2 F_0 \omega}{(s^2 + \omega^2)\Delta(s)},$$

of which the steady state is

(5) $$L^{-1}\left\{\frac{k_2 F_0 \omega}{\Delta(i\omega)(s^2 + \omega^2)}\right\} = -\frac{F_0}{k_2} \sin \omega t.$$

Thus the absorber oscillates with the frequency of the exciting force

† See J. V. Uspensky, *Theory of Equations* (New York, McGraw-Hill, 1948), p. 304, for the "Hurwitz criterion".

and has an amplitude equal to the elongation of the spring k_2 under a force F_0.

Example 2. *Automobile spring system and analog.* Analogous mechanical and electrical systems are shown in Figs. 38 and 39, each having two degrees of freedom. The mechanical system can be considered as

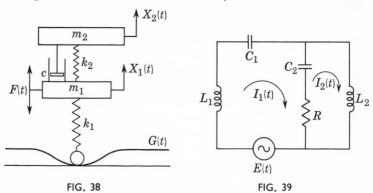

FIG. 38   FIG. 39

an idealization of an automobile suspension system. The chassis is represented by mass m_2, the shock absorbers and body springs by the damping system c and spring k_2, the wheel and axle by mass m_1 and the flexible tire by spring k_1. The road irregularities impart the forcing function $F(t)$ through the tire to the axle system. This may be due to a road irregularity $G(t)$. What can be done to make the motion of m_2 to be as smooth as possible?

The differential equations for the system illustrated in Fig. 38 are

(6) $$\begin{cases} m_1 X_1'' + k_1(X_1 - G) + k_2(X_1 - X_2) + c(X_1' - X_2') = 0, \\ m_2 X_2 + c(X_2' - X_1') + k_2(X_2 - X_1) = 0. \end{cases}$$

With zero initial conditions, these equations have the transforms

(7) $$\begin{cases} (m_1 s^2 + cs + k_1 + k_2)x_1(s) - (cs + k_2)x_2(s) = k_1 g(s), \\ -(cs + k_2)x_1(s) + (m_2 s^2 + cs + k_2)x_2(s) = 0. \end{cases}$$

At this stage we may be interested in several items. What are the motions of the masses? What is the force in the spring k_2? Can the mass m_1 have motion relative to the road such that the tire will leave the road? When the automobile strikes a sharp bump, how does the corresponding "jerk" on mass m_2 affect the riding comfort?

If system (7) is solved for $x_1(s)$ and $x_2(s)$, then their inverses give the motions $X_1(t)$ and $X_2(t)$. Similarly the force in the spring k_2 is found from the relative deflection of the masses, and the transform of this force is $k_2[x_1(s) - x_2(s)]$. Obviously this involves $g(s)$ and thus the spring force depends on the road roughness. Again if we know the displacement of the axle relative to the road and if this displacement exceeds the static deflection of spring k_1 under the total load $m_1 + m_2$, the tire will leave the road. Hence if one finds the value of the transform $x_1(s) - g(s)$ then its inverse will give the relative displacement which is involved.

Finally if $X_2(t)$ is the motion of the body of the car, its riding comfort is certainly impaired if the change of acceleration, that is, $X_2'''(t)$, is very rapid or sudden enough to produce a "jerk". Now the transform of $X_2'''(t)$ is $s^3 x_2(s)$ if proper initial conditions exist at $t = 0$. If at $t = 0$ the tire receives the impact of a road obstruction simulated by the step function $G_0 \mathscr{U}(t)$, where G_0 is a constant, then we wish to find how $X_2'''(t)$ behaves at $t = 0$. This "jerk" can be determined if we recall a theorem [Theorem XI, §2.8] to the effect that $\lim\limits_{s \to \infty} sf(s) = \lim\limits_{t \to 0^+} F(t)$, where $L\{F(t)\} = f(s)$. Here we take $F(t)$ to be $X'''(t)$ and observe that

(8)
$$\lim_{t \to 0^+} X'''(t) = \lim_{s \to \infty} s[s^3 x_2(s)]$$

$$= \lim_{s \to \infty} \frac{s^3 k_1 G_0 (cs + k_2)}{(m_1 s^2 + cs + k_1 + k_2)(m_2 s^2 + cs + k_2) - (cs + k_2)^2}$$

$$= \frac{k_1 c G_0}{m_1 m_2}.$$

This is the magnitude of the "jerk". Thus the riding comfort is improved by flexible tires with small values of k_1, small damping c, and large masses m_1 and m_2. If c is large, that is, if we approach a rigid connection between body and axle, then an infinite "jerk" will result.

EXERCISES 2

1. In system (1), let $F(t) = 3 \sin 2t$. If the vibration damper has "clearance" for vibrating with an amplitude of only one unit, what are the values of k_2 and m_2?

2. In system (7), set $c = 0$, $g(s) = \omega/(s^2 + \omega^2)$, and find $x_1(s)$ and $x_2(s)$.

3. In 2 set $m_1 = m_2 = k_2 = 1$, $k_1 = 2$ and $\omega = 1$, then find the frequencies of vibration of the resultant motion.

4.5 AUTOMATIC CONTROL MECHANISMS

Automatic regulatory devices are common installations in systems in which control of pressure, of flow, of speed, or of any output function is of prime importance. Such controllers are used to regulate temperature, voltage, frequency, stabilize ships, pilot aircraft, and control amplification and waveform in vacuum tube

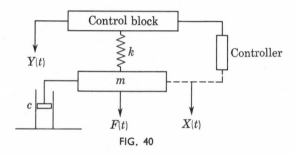

FIG. 40

amplifiers. When an output function deviates from a desired value, this transient deviation is translated by a detector to a control of the input function thereby restoring the output to its normal value. The device which corrects the input function is called a *controller*. As is shown below, the over-all system will be stable and non-oscillatory in the steady state if the characteristic equation has roots with only negative real parts, although it will be stable but oscillatory if the conjugate imaginary roots are all different. It will be unstable if there are roots with positive real parts, or if zero or conjugate imaginary roots are repeated.

In Fig. 40 a mechanical system has a mass mounted with spring and damping element. The mass is spring-connected with a control block whose position is variable. The controller detects any deviations $X(t)$ of the mass m from a reference position and translates this to the control block by a relation

$$(1) \qquad Y(t) = -hX(t) - r \int_0^t X(t) \, dt,$$

where h, r are positive constants. This equation states that the instantaneous correcting displacement $Y(t)$ is dependent upon both the instantaneous motion $X(t)$ and the previous motion of m. When $X(t)$ is positive, the control block has correcting negative displacement. Assuming the system is initially at rest, we have the integro-differential system and its transforms as follows:

$$(2) \quad \begin{cases} mX''(t) + cX'(t) + k(X(t) - Y(t)) = F(t), \\ Y(t) + hX(t) + r \int_0^t X(t)\, dt = 0, \end{cases}$$

$$(3) \quad \begin{cases} (ms^2 + cs + k)x(s) - ky(s) = f(s), \\ \left(h + \dfrac{r}{s}\right)x(s) + y(s) = 0. \end{cases}$$

Solving for $x(s)$, we obtain

$$(4) \quad x(s) = \frac{f(s)}{ms^2 + cs + k + k\left(h + \dfrac{r}{s}\right)}.$$

The denominator of (4) is the characteristic transform $\Phi(s)$ of the system. When (4) is written in rational fractional form, the denominator is a cubic and of course has three zeros. The nature of these zeros and the zeros of $f(s)$ determines the output function $X(t)$ and hence the stability of the system. In the case $F(t) = F_0 \mathcal{U}(t)$, we have $f(s) = F_0/s$, and equation (4) is

$$(5) \quad x(s) = F_0/[ms^3 + cs^2 + k(1 + h)s + kr].$$

Further, if $r = 0$, then the controller in Fig. 40 is a *proportional deviation controller*; otherwise it is a *proportional plus integrating controller*. For $r = 0$, equation (5) yields

$$(6) \quad x(s) = \frac{F_0/(k + kh)}{s} + \frac{As + B}{ms^2 + cs + k + kh},$$

where A and B are appropriate constants. Since $c > 0$, there is positive damping and the transient terms arising from the second fraction of (6) will be damped out. Hence a final constant output $X(t)$ persists which is called the *load error*. Although oscillations can occur when $c^2 - 4m(k + kh) < 0$, they will be damped out by the factor $e^{-ct/2m}$. When r is greater than zero, then $\Phi(s)$ has no zero, so that the load error vanishes.

EXERCISES 3

1. Write the cubic equation whose roots determine the stability of the inverse of (5) if $h = 0$. Discuss the stability for this case if $m = 1$ and $r = c > 0$.

2. Write the system of equations of the form (2) if the resistance element (c in Fig. 40) is connected between m and the control block. Write the characteristic equation of the system for $F(t) = F_0 \mathscr{U}(t)$.

3. Study system (2) if the integral in the second equation of (2) is replaced by dX/dt; that is, the controller equation is $Y(t) + hX(t) + rX'(t) = 0$. Consider the case $F(t) = F_0 \mathscr{U}(t)$, F_0 a constant.

4. A flow level controller system is sketched in Fig. 41. The

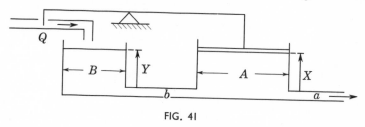

FIG. 41

cross-sectional areas of the containers are A and B, the flow coefficients of the tubes connected with A are a and b. The variable input flow Q governed by the controller is

$$Q = aX_0 + h(X - X_0) + r \int_0^t (X - X_0)\, dt,$$

where X_0 is the mean level desired in A. Use the equations

$$AX' = aX + b(Y - X),$$
$$BY' = Q + b(X - Y),$$
$$X(0) = Y(0) = 0,$$

to find $x(s)$ and the final value of $X(t)$ as t approaches infinity.

4.6 STRUCTURAL APPLICATIONS

In the study of structural elements the transform method offers a simple approach, since discontinuous loads, concentrated loads and external bending couples may be expressed by use of unit functions, impulse functions and doublet functions, respectively. For such problems the space coordinate x plays the role formerly played by the time t, and the transforms are now taken with respect to the variable x.

From the elementary theory of strength of materials it is known that the load-bearing capacity of a beam is given by

(1) $$A \frac{d^4 Y}{dx^4} = \text{load} = F(x),$$

where $Y(x)$ is the deflection, $\dfrac{dY}{dx}$ is the slope, and

$$-A \frac{d^2 Y}{dx^2} = \text{internal bending moment} = M(x),$$

$$-A \frac{d^3 Y}{dx^3} = \text{shearing force} = V(x).$$

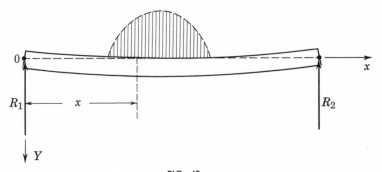

FIG. 42

In equation (1) A is the flexural rigidity of the beam and is equal to the product of Young's modulus and the moment of inertia (about the neutral axis) of the cross section of the beam.

The x-coordinate can be measured from any section of the beam, but for purposes of this brief analysis we shall measure it from the left end of the beam. The x-axis itself is a line representing a neutral axis of the undeformed beam. A downward deflection $Y(x)$ from this line shall be considered as positive. A bending moment causing compression in the top half of the beam is considered as positive. This is apparent from Fig. 42, because positive $M(x)$ by the above definition requires that the function $d^2 Y/dx^2$ be negative. Applied loads $F(x)$ directed downward are also considered positive. The vertical shear $V(x)$ at a section at x is positive if the resultant of the forces acting on the portion of the beam to the right of the section is downward.

The transform method will be applied to the cantilever beam of Fig. 43, that is, to a beam built in at the end $x = 0$. The associated differential equation is

$$A\frac{d^4 Y}{dx^4} = w_0 \mathcal{U}(x) - w_0 \mathcal{U}\left(x - \frac{a}{2}\right) + P\mathcal{I}\left(x - \frac{2a}{3}\right),$$

where w_0 is a load per unit length and $P\mathcal{I}$ is a point load of weight P acting at $x = \frac{2}{3}a$. The Laplace transform of this equation is

$$A[s^4 y(s) - s^3 Y(0) - s^2 Y'(0) - s Y''(0) - Y'''(0)]$$
$$= \frac{w_0}{s}\left(1 - e^{-\frac{sa}{2}}\right) + Pe^{-\frac{2sa}{3}},$$

where $y(s) = L\{Y(x)\}$. Hence

(2)
$$Ay(s) = \frac{w_0}{s^5}\left(1 - e^{-\frac{sa}{2}}\right) + \frac{P}{s^4}e^{-\frac{2sa}{3}}$$
$$+ A\left[\frac{Y(0)}{s} + \frac{Y'(0)}{s^2} + \frac{Y''(0)}{s^3} + \frac{Y'''(0)}{s^4}\right].$$

Since there is no deflection and no slope at the clamped end, two boundary conditions are $Y(0) = Y'(0) = 0$. Also at $x = 0$, the moment is $M(0) = -2P\frac{a}{3} - w_0\left(\frac{a}{2}\right)\left(\frac{a}{4}\right)$ and hence

$$A Y''(0) = 2P\frac{a}{3} + w_0\frac{a^2}{8}.$$

Also, we have

$$A Y'''(0) = -\left(P + w_0\frac{a}{2}\right).$$

Making use of these boundary conditions in (2) we get

$$Ay(s) = \frac{w_0}{s^5}\left(1 - e^{-\frac{sa}{2}}\right) + \frac{Pe^{-\frac{2sa}{3}}}{s^4}$$
$$+ P\left(\frac{2a}{3s^3} - \frac{1}{s^4}\right) + \frac{w_0 a}{2}\left(\frac{a}{4s^3} - \frac{1}{s^4}\right).$$

The inverse transform of this equation is

$$A\,Y(x) = \frac{w_0 x^4}{24} - \frac{w_0}{24}\,\mathcal{U}\left(x - \frac{a}{2}\right)\left(x - \frac{a}{2}\right)^4$$

$$+ \frac{P}{6}\,\mathcal{U}\left(x - \frac{2a}{3}\right)\left(x - \frac{2a}{3}\right)^3 + P\left(\frac{2ax^2}{6} - \frac{x^3}{6}\right)$$

$$+ \frac{w_0 a}{2}\left(\frac{ax^2}{8} - \frac{x^3}{6}\right).$$

This function may also be written in the form

$$(3)\quad A\,Y(x) = B(x),\qquad \left(0 \le x \le \frac{a}{2}\right),$$

$$= B(x) - \frac{w_0}{24}\left(x - \frac{a}{2}\right)^4,\qquad \left(\frac{a}{2} \le x \le \frac{2a}{3}\right),$$

$$= B(x) - \frac{w_0}{24}\left(x - \frac{a}{2}\right)^4 + \frac{P}{6}\left(x - \frac{2a}{3}\right)^3,\qquad \left(\frac{2a}{3} \le x \le a\right),$$

where

$$B(x) = \frac{w_0}{24}\,(x^4 - 2x^3 a + \tfrac{3}{2}x^2 a^2) + \frac{Px^2}{6}\,(2a - x).$$

The reader may verify that the deflection is continuous and satisfies $Y(0) = Y'(0) = Y''(a) = Y'''(a) = 0$. In fact the last line of (3) shows that the deflection is a linear function of x for $x > \dfrac{2a}{3}$, hence the beam remains straight for x in the interval $\left(\dfrac{2a}{3}, a\right)$. If the values of $Y''(0)$ and $Y'''(0)$ had not been given, then they would have appeared in equation (3). In this case, the requirement that $Y''(a) = Y'''(a) = 0$ would suffice to determine the constants $Y''(0)$ and $Y'''(0)$. This procedure enables one to find the deflection of a beam clamped at both ends.

In particular, it should be noted that the transform method requires no more than a single differential equation valid over the entire length of the beam. This is in contrast to the ordinary method of having a separate equation for each interval between successive discontinuities of the loading.

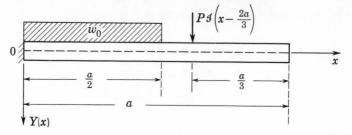

FIG. 43

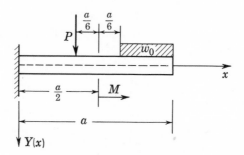

FIG. 44

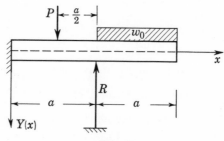

FIG. 45

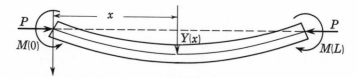

FIG. 46

EXERCISES 4

1. Find the function which describes the deflection of the last third of the beam of Fig. 43.

2. The beam represented in Fig. 44 is clamped at both ends and loaded as illustrated. Find the deflection curve and the moment at the end $x = 0$. (Use the doublet $M\mathscr{D}(x - a/2)$. See p. 82.)

3. In Fig. 45 the cantilever beam has a fixed reaction R at $x = a$. Determine its value so that there is no deflection at $x = a$.

4. In Fig. 46 a column of length L has end loads and moments which cause buckling under critical loads P. From equation (1), §4.6, the moment equation at a section x is

$$-A \frac{d^2 Y}{dx^2} = PY - M(0).$$

Write the transformed equation and show

$$Y(x) = \frac{Y'(0)}{\beta} \sin \beta x + \frac{M(0)}{A\beta^2} (1 - \cos \beta x), \qquad (\beta^2 = P/A).$$

For pinned ends, that is, fixed ends free to rotate about an axis perpendicular to the xY-plane, the boundary conditions are

$$Y(0) = Y(L) = M(0) = M(L) = 0.$$

In this case show that $P = \dfrac{\pi^2 A}{L^2}$.

For clamped ends, the boundary conditions are $Y(0) = Y(L) = Y'(0) = Y'(L) = 0$. Show that $P = 4\pi^2 A/L^2$.

5

Applications to Linear Partial
Differential Equations

··

5.1 INTRODUCTION

Many of the problems considered in mathematics have their
origins in the physical sciences and engineering and are of such
nature that they require the solution of partial differential equations
subject to certain additional conditions.   Although many of these
equations are non-linear and thus do not succumb to treatment by
the Laplace transform method, there is still a large number of
problems that lead to the consideration of linear partial differential
equations with constant coefficients.   In the latter case, the Laplace
transform does provide a useful and important method for finding
the solution.   In this chapter, we shall not question the existence of
the solution to any of our problems, since the physical counterpart
will require that there be a solution, and in fact, only one solution.
Thus our treatment will be a formal one and the existence of the
solution of a given problem will be established by exhibiting it
explicitly.   This, of course, still leaves unanswered the question as
to whether the solution obtained is the only one.   We shall not
attempt to answer such questions here but shall concentrate upon
obtaining a solution and leave the question of uniqueness to later
courses in mathematics.

As mentioned above, the complete mathematical statement of a
physical problem, or the approximation thereto, requires that the
solution of the differential equation satisfy certain specified conditions for given values of the independent variables.   Such conditions are known as boundary conditions and the differential

equation along with these boundary conditions constitutes what is known as a *boundary value problem*. So in this chapter we shall be concerned with finding solutions of certain boundary value problems.

5.2 PARTIAL TRANSFORMS

Before considering any particular problems, we shall discuss what is meant by the Laplace transform of a function $F(x, t)$ of two independent variables x and t. Since there are two independent variables we may treat one as a parameter, say x, and take the Laplace transform of $F(x, t)$ as though it were a function of t alone. Then the partial Laplace transform of $F(x, t)$ with respect to t is formally analogous to the transform of a function of the single variable t and is defined by

$$(1) \qquad L_t\{F(x, t)\} = \int_0^\infty e^{-st} F(x, t)\, dt = f(x, s).$$

In (1) the subscript t indicates that the transform is taken with respect to the variable t. Since x is treated here as a parameter, the various theorems given in the preceding chapters are formally applicable. For example, if we want $L_t\left\{\dfrac{\partial F(x, t)}{\partial t}\right\}$, it is given (under suitable assumptions on $F(x, t)$) by

$$L_t\left\{\frac{\partial F(x, t)}{\partial t}\right\} = sL_t\{F(x, t)\} - F(x, 0).$$

The situation is somewhat different when we consider partial differentiation with respect to x. If we want $L_t\left\{\dfrac{\partial F(x, t)}{\partial x}\right\}$, then by definition (1) we have

$$(2) \qquad L_t\left\{\frac{\partial F(x, t)}{\partial x}\right\} = \int_0^\infty e^{-st} \frac{\partial F(x, t)}{\partial x}\, dt$$

$$= \frac{\partial}{\partial x} \int_0^\infty e^{-st} F(x, t)\, dt$$

$$= \frac{\partial f(x, s)}{\partial x},$$

provided it is permissible to interchange the order of integration and differentiation. In what follows we shall assume that our functions are such that transforming with respect to t and differentiating with respect to x are commutative operations. The next few sections illustrate the use of the partial Laplace transform defined by (1).

EXERCISES I

1. If $F(x, t) = ax + bt$, where a and b are constants, show that:

(a) $L_t\left\{\dfrac{\partial}{\partial x} F(x, t)\right\} = \dfrac{\partial}{\partial x} L_t\{F(x, t)\}.$

(b) $L_t\left\{\dfrac{\partial}{\partial t} F(x, t)\right\} = sL_t\{F(x, t)\} - F(x, 0).$

2. If $F(x, t) = \sin \omega(x - t)$, show that

$$L_t\left\{\dfrac{\partial^2}{\partial x^2} F(x, t)\right\} = \dfrac{\partial^2}{\partial x^2} L_t\{\sin \omega(x - t)\}.$$

5.3 THE SEMI-INFINITE STRING

Let a long string be stretched along the x-axis with one end at the origin and let x and Y denote the coordinates of any point on the string at time t, so that the transverse displacement Y is a function $Y(x, t)$. Then the differential equation† satisfied by $Y(x, t)$ is

$$(1) \qquad \frac{\partial^2 Y(x, t)}{\partial t^2} = a^2 \frac{\partial^2 Y(x, t)}{\partial x^2}, \qquad (x > 0, t > 0),$$

where $a = \sqrt{T/\rho}$, is called the *propagation constant*, T being the tension in the string and ρ the mass per unit length. Let us further require that $Y(x, t)$ satisfy the boundary conditions

$$(2) \qquad\qquad Y(0, t) = F(t), \qquad (t \geq 0),$$
$$\lim_{x \to \infty} Y(x, t) = 0, \qquad (t \geq 0).$$

The first condition gives the displacement of the end of the string as a function of time, and the second condition implies that at any

† A development of this and other partial differential equations which occur in this chapter may be found in C. R. Wylie, Jr., *Advanced Engineering Mathematics* (New York, McGraw-Hill, 1951), pp. 199–210.

fixed time the motion dies away as we go out along the string. In order to keep our problem simple we require that $F(t)$ have continuous second derivatives and be such that $F(0) = 0$. In addition we shall require that the initial displacement and the initial velocity be zero, that is,

$$(3) \qquad\qquad Y(x, 0) = 0, \qquad (x \geq 0),$$

$$\frac{\partial Y(x, 0)}{\partial t} = 0, \qquad (x > 0).$$

The differential equation (1) along with the boundary conditions (2) and the initial conditions (3) constitutes our boundary value problem.

Now let $y(x, s)$ denote the Laplace transform of $Y(x, t)$ with respect to t. Then the transform of the left-hand side of equation (1) is

$$(4) \qquad L_t\left\{\frac{\partial^2 Y(x, t)}{\partial t^2}\right\} = s^2 y(x, s) - \frac{\partial Y(x, 0)}{\partial t} - s Y(x, 0)$$

$$= s^2 y(x, s),$$

where we have used conditions (3) to get the last result. Thus, by use of an extension of (2), §5.2 the partial differential equation (1) is transformed into the differential equation

$$(5) \qquad\qquad s^2 y(x, s) = a^2 \frac{d^2 y(x, s)}{dx^2}$$

for the transform $y(x, s)$, where we are using the symbol for ordinary differentiation since here we are regarding s as a parameter. The solution of equation (5) is

$$(6) \qquad\qquad y(x, s) = A(s) e^{\frac{s}{a} x} + B(s) e^{-\frac{s}{a} x},$$

where the "constants" of integration may depend upon the parameter $s > 0$. Now if we transform the first of equations (2) we get

$$(7) \qquad L\{Y(0, t)\} = y(0, s) = L\{F(t)\} = f(s).$$

Then equations (6) and (7) give

$$(8) \qquad\qquad f(s) = A(s) + B(s).$$

Applying the transform to the second equation of (2) we have

$$(9) \qquad\qquad \lim_{x \to \infty} y(x, s) = 0,$$

provided it is permissible to interchange the order of integration and the limit process. This last condition (9) implies that $A(s)$ must be zero, since $e^{sx/a}$ approaches infinity as x approaches infinity. Therefore conditions (8) and (9) imply that the solution to the ordinary differential equation (5) may be written in the form

$$(10) \qquad\qquad y(x, s) = f(s)e^{-\frac{s}{a}x}.$$

By our translation property, Theorem XII, §3.3, we may write the inverse transform of $y(x, s)$ at once to get

$$(11) \qquad Y(x, t) = F\left(t - \frac{x}{a}\right), \qquad \left(t \geq \frac{x}{a}\right),$$

$$= 0, \qquad \left(t < \frac{x}{a}\right).$$

Expressed in terms of the unit functions,

$$(12) \qquad Y(x, t) = F\left(t - \frac{x}{a}\right) \mathcal{U}\left(t - \frac{x}{a}\right).$$

Either one of the forms (11) or (12) may be taken as the solution of our boundary value problem.

As mentioned previously, we should verify that (12) is in fact a solution of our problem. It is easy to see that any function of $t - \dfrac{x}{a}$ is a solution of the differential equation (1) as long as it has second derivatives. For consider a function of u, say $H(u)$, which possesses a second derivative. Then for $u = t - \dfrac{x}{a}$,

$$\frac{\partial H}{\partial x} = -\frac{1}{a} H'\left(t - \frac{x}{a}\right), \qquad \frac{\partial^2 H}{\partial x^2} = \frac{1}{a^2} H''\left(t - \frac{x}{a}\right),$$

$$\frac{\partial H}{\partial t} = H'\left(t - \frac{x}{a}\right), \qquad \frac{\partial^2 H}{\partial t^2} = H''\left(t - \frac{x}{a}\right),$$

where the prime denotes differentiation with respect to the argument $t - \dfrac{x}{a}$. Thus if $Y(x, t)$ in (1) is replaced by $H\left(t - \dfrac{x}{a}\right)$, it is clear that this function satisfies that differential equation. In particular if we take Y to be that function of $t - \dfrac{x}{a}$ which is given by (12), then equation (1) is satisfied† in view of the conditions on $F(t)$.

We must verify not only that (12) is a solution of the differential equation but also that it satisfies the conditions (2) and (3). The first of equations (2) is satisfied for if we set $x = 0$ in (12) we get $Y(0, t) = F(t)$. The second of equations (2) is satisfied because

$$\mathscr{U}\left(t - \frac{x}{a}\right) = 0 \text{ for } t - \frac{x}{a} < 0, \text{ and given any } t, \; t - \frac{x}{a} < 0 \text{ when}$$

$x > at$. The first of equations (3) is satisfied since $\mathscr{U}\left(-\dfrac{x}{a}\right) = 0$

for $x > 0$, and $Y(0, 0) = F(0) = 0$, by assumption. To verify the last condition we compute with $x \neq at$

$$\frac{\partial Y(x, t)}{\partial t} = F'\left(t - \frac{x}{a}\right)\mathscr{U}\left(t - \frac{x}{a}\right),$$

and again for $t = 0$, $\mathscr{U}\left(-\dfrac{x}{a}\right) = 0$ for $x > 0$.

5.4   THE VIBRATING STRING

Let us consider a stretched string of finite length L held fixed at both ends and given an initial displacement $C \sin \dfrac{\pi x}{L}$ and zero initial velocity. Here we have

$$(1) \qquad \frac{\partial^2 Y(x, t)}{\partial t^2} = a^2 \frac{\partial^2 Y(x, t)}{\partial x^2}, \qquad (0 \leq x \leq L, t \geq 0),$$

$$(2) \qquad Y(0, t) = Y(L, t) = 0, \qquad (t \geq 0),$$

$$(3) \qquad Y(x, 0) = C \sin \frac{\pi x}{L}, \qquad (0 \leq x \leq L),$$

$$(4) \qquad \frac{\partial Y(x, 0)}{\partial t} = 0, \qquad (0 \leq x \leq L).$$

† It should be noted that our solution (12) may not satisfy equation (1) everywhere because its derivatives may not exist when $x = at$. Nevertheless, (12) is commonly regarded as the solution of this problem, even when $F'(t)$ is discontinuous.

If we apply the Laplace transform to equation (1) and use (3) and (4), we get

$$(5) \qquad a^2 \frac{d^2y(x, s)}{dx^2} = s^2y(x, s) - sC \sin \frac{\pi x}{L}.$$

This is an ordinary differential equation in y and x in which s plays the role of a parameter. The associated boundary conditions are found by taking the Laplace transform of conditions (2), that is,

$$(6) \qquad y(0, s) = y(L, s) = 0.$$

The general solution of (5) is

$$(7) \qquad y(x, s) = A(s) \cosh \frac{sx}{a} + B(s) \sinh \frac{sx}{a} + \frac{sC \sin \dfrac{\pi x}{L}}{s^2 + \dfrac{a^2\pi^2}{L^2}}.$$

The conditions (6) imply that $A(s) = B(s) = 0$, so that the solution of the transformed problem is

$$(8) \qquad y(x, s) = \frac{sC}{s^2 + \dfrac{a^2\pi^2}{L^2}} \sin \frac{\pi x}{L}.$$

In order to get the solution of our original problem we must find the inverse transform of $y(x, s)$, but this is easily seen to be

$$(9) \qquad Y(x, t) = L_t^{-1}\{y(x, s)\} = C \cos \frac{a\pi t}{L} \sin \frac{\pi x}{L}.$$

The student should verify that this is in fact the solution of the problem given by (1), (2), (3), and (4).

EXERCISES 2

1. Let a semi-infinite string be stretched along the x-axis with one end at the origin and let it be initially at rest in this position. Now let the end $x = 0$ be given a motion described by the function $F(t) = 2 \sin 3t$. Determine the motion of the string for $t > 0$ and $x > 0$.

2. A string of unit length is stretched between two fixed points in the (x, y)-plane, the origin and $(1, 0)$.   The density and tension are such that the propagation constant a is 1.   If it is given an initial velocity of $\sin \pi x$, determine the subsequent motion of the string.

3. Suppose that the string in 2 is released from rest from an initial configuration of the form of the parabola $F(x) = x - x^2$. What is the transform $y(x, s)$ of its subsequent motion?

4. If a string is stretched in a horizontal position and the weight of the string is taken into account then the differential equation (1), §5.4 must be replaced by the equation.

$$(1a) \qquad \frac{\partial^2 Y(x, t)}{\partial t^2} = a^2 \frac{\partial^2 Y(x, t)}{\partial x^2} - g,$$

where g is the acceleration due to gravity.   Suppose that a heavy string of length L is stretched between two fixed points in a horizontal plane in such a way that conditions (2), (3), and (4) of §5.4 hold. Determine the transform $y(x, s)$ of the motion of the string.

5. Suppose that a semi-infinite heavy string is subjected to the conditions

$$Y(x, 0) = \frac{\partial Y(x, 0)}{\partial t} = 0, \qquad (x > 0),$$

$$Y(0, t) = 0, \quad \lim_{x \to \infty} \frac{\partial Y(x, t)}{\partial x} = 0, \qquad (t > 0).$$

Find the solution of the resulting boundary value problem.   (Note: the last condition might be approximated by fixing the distant end of a long string to a ring free to slide on a vertical rod with no friction.)

5.5 LONGITUDINAL VIBRATIONS OF A BAR

The partial differential equation which governs longitudinal vibrations in a uniform bar of length L with one end fixed at the origin is

$$(1) \quad a^2 \frac{\partial^2 V(x, t)}{\partial x^2} = \frac{\partial^2 V(x, t)}{\partial t^2}, \qquad \left(t \geq 0, 0 \leq x \leq L, a^2 = \frac{E}{\rho} \right),$$

where $V(x, t)$ represents the displacement of the cross section of the bar at position x at time t. If the bar is unstrained and at rest initially, then the initial conditions are

(2) $$V(x, 0) = 0, \qquad (0 \leq x \leq L),$$

$$\frac{\partial V(x, 0)}{\partial t} = 0, \qquad (0 \leq x \leq L).$$

Further, since we have specified that one end is fixed at the origin, we have

(3) $$V(0, t) = 0, \qquad (t \geq 0).$$

A constant force F_0 acting longitudinally is applied to the free end and we wish to determine the displacement $V(L, t)$ of the free end. Then the fourth boundary condition is

(4) $$\frac{\partial V(L, t)}{\partial x} = \frac{F_0}{E}, \qquad (t \geq 0),$$

where E is Young's modulus.

If we denote by $v(x, s)$ the transform of $V(x, t)$ with respect to t, then the transform of equation (1), using conditions (2) becomes

(5) $$a^2 \frac{d^2 v(x, s)}{dx^2} = s^2 v(x, s).$$

The transformed boundary conditions associated with this equation are

(6) $$v(0, s) = 0, \qquad \frac{dv(L, s)}{dx} = \frac{F_0}{Es}.$$

Now the general solution of equation (5) is

(7) $$v(x, s) = A(s)e^{\frac{sx}{a}} + B(s)e^{-\frac{sx}{a}},$$

so the first of conditions (6) implies that

(8) $$B(s) = -A(s),$$

and the second of (6) gives

(9) $$\frac{F_0}{Es} = \frac{s}{a} A(s)e^{\frac{sL}{a}} - \frac{s}{a} B(s)e^{-\frac{sL}{a}}.$$

These last two equations give

(10) $$A(s) = -B(s) = \frac{aF_0}{Es^2} \frac{1}{e^{\frac{sL}{a}} + e^{-\frac{sL}{a}}}.$$

Therefore the solution of (5) which satisfies conditions (6) may be written

$$(11) \qquad v(x, s) = \frac{aF_0}{Es^2} \cdot \frac{\sinh \dfrac{sx}{a}}{\cosh \dfrac{sL}{a}} .$$

Since we are interested in the displacement of the free end, we set $x = L$ in (11) to obtain

$$(12) \qquad v(L, s) = \frac{aF_0}{Es^2} \tanh \frac{sL}{a} .$$

The inverse transform of this type of function was found in §3.5, Example 3, to be the triangle function whose graph is exhibited in Fig. 47.   Thus we see that the free end undergoes a periodic motion made up of a series of jerks as indicated in Fig. 47.

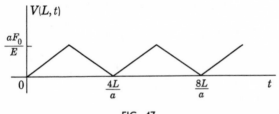

FIG. 47

If we wish to determine the motion of a general cross section of the bar located at the position x we may proceed as follows.   Returning to the result given in (11) and setting $\dfrac{aF_0}{E} = C$ for convenience, we have

$$(13) \qquad v(x, s) = \frac{C}{s^2} \frac{\sinh \dfrac{sx}{a}}{\cosh \dfrac{sL}{a}} = \frac{C}{s^2} \frac{e^{\frac{sx}{a}} - e^{-\frac{sx}{a}}}{e^{\frac{sL}{a}} + e^{-\frac{sL}{a}}}$$

$$= \frac{C}{s^2} \frac{e^{-\frac{(L-x)s}{a}} - e^{-\frac{(L+x)s}{a}}}{1 + e^{-\frac{2sL}{a}}} .$$

Now if we make use of the fact that the sum of a geometric series $1 + r + r^2 + \cdots$ is given by $\dfrac{1}{1-r}$ for $|r| < 1$, the factor $\dfrac{1}{1 + e^{-\frac{2sL}{a}}}$ may be written

$$\frac{1}{1 + e^{-\frac{2sL}{a}}} = \sum_{k=0}^{\infty} (-1)^k e^{-\frac{2sLk}{a}}.$$

Therefore $v(x, s)$ may be put in the form

$$(14) \qquad v(x, s) = \frac{C}{s^2}\left[e^{-\frac{(L-x)}{a}s} - e^{-\frac{(L+x)}{a}s} \right] \sum_{k=0}^{\infty} (-1)^k e^{-\frac{2Lsk}{a}}$$

$$= C \sum_{k=0}^{\infty} \frac{(-1)^k}{s^2} \left[e^{-\frac{s}{a}[(2k+1)L-x]} - e^{-\frac{s}{a}[(2k+1)L+x]} \right].$$

Now taking the inverse transform term by term, we get

$$V(x, t) = C \sum_{k=0}^{\infty} (-1)^k \left[\left(t - \frac{(2k+1)L - x}{a} \right) \mathcal{U}\left(t - \frac{(2k+1)L - x}{a} \right) \right.$$

$$(15)$$

$$\left. - \left(t - \frac{(2k+1)L + x}{a} \right) \mathcal{U}\left(t - \frac{(2k+1)L + x}{a} \right) \right].$$

The quantities $\dfrac{(2k+1)L - x}{a}$ and $\dfrac{(2k+1)L + x}{a}$ will be greater than t for any fixed value of t, for k sufficiently large. Since $\mathcal{U}(t - t_0) = 0$ for $t - t_0 < 0$, the number of non-zero terms in the expression for $V(x, t)$ is finite for any fixed t. Of course the number of non-zero terms increases as t increases. For any fixed x, the graph of $V(x, t)$ is easily obtainable. To indicate how this graph is obtained, we write out explicitly the first few terms in (15); that is,

$$(16) \quad V(x, t) = C\left\{ \left(t - \frac{L - x}{a} \right) \mathcal{U}\left(t - \frac{L - x}{a} \right) \right.$$

$$- \left(t - \frac{L + x}{a} \right) \mathcal{U}\left(t - \frac{L + x}{a} \right) - \left(t - \frac{3L - x}{a} \right) \mathcal{U}\left(t - \frac{3L - x}{a} \right)$$

$$\left. + \left(t - \frac{3L + x}{a} \right) \mathcal{U}\left(t - \frac{3L + x}{a} \right) + \cdots \right\}.$$

Making use of our knowledge of the unit functions we see that

$$
\begin{aligned}
(17)\qquad V(x, t) &= 0, && \left(0 \leq t < \frac{L-x}{a}\right), \\
&= t - \frac{L-x}{a}, && \left(\frac{L-x}{a} \leq t < \frac{L+x}{a}\right), \\
&= \frac{2x}{a}, && \left(\frac{L+x}{a} \leq t < \frac{3L-x}{a}\right), \\
&= -t + \frac{3L+x}{a}, && \left(\frac{3L-x}{a} \leq t < \frac{3L+x}{a}\right), \\
&\;\;\vdots && \qquad\qquad \vdots
\end{aligned}
$$

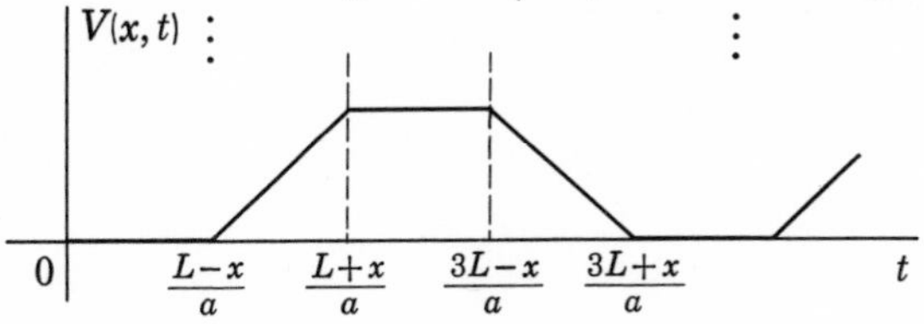

FIG. 48

The graph of $V(x, t)$ is given in Fig. 48. The verification that $V(x, t)$ is the solution of our problem will not be made here.

EXERCISES 3

1. Let the right-hand side of equation (4) be replaced by the function

$$
\begin{aligned}
F(t) &= 1, && (t < t_0), \\
&= 0, && (t \geq t_0),
\end{aligned}
$$

while the remaining conditions on the bar are the same as those given in §5.5. Study the resulting vibration of the bar.

2. A uniform bar of length L has one end fixed at the origin. Suppose that it is stretched uniformly to a new length L_0 and released from this position at time $t = 0$. Determine the displacement $V(x, t)$ of any cross section. In particular determine the motion of the free end of the bar. [The displacement $V(x, t)$ of any section satisfies

$$\frac{\partial^2 V(x, t)}{\partial t^2} = a^2 \frac{\partial^2 V(x, t)}{\partial^2 x} \qquad (0 \leq x \leq L, t \geq 0),$$

$$V(x, 0) = \frac{L_0 - L}{L} x, \quad \frac{\partial V(x, 0)}{\partial t} = 0, \qquad (0 \leq x \leq L),$$

$$V(0, t) = 0, \quad \frac{\partial V(L, t)}{\partial x} = 0, \qquad (t \geq 0).]$$

5.6 HEAT CONDUCTION

One of the simpler problems of heat conduction requires the solution of the boundary value problem

$$(1) \qquad \frac{\partial U(x, t)}{\partial t} = a \frac{\partial^2 U(x, t)}{\partial x^2}, \qquad (t \geq 0, x > 0),$$

$$(2) \qquad U(x, 0) = 0, \qquad (x > 0),$$

$$(3) \qquad U(0, t) = U_0, \qquad (t > 0),$$

$$(4) \qquad \lim_{x \to \infty} U(x, t) = 0, \qquad (t \geq 0).$$

We may take as our physical model for this problem a semi-infinite homogeneous solid with $x \geq 0$, bounded by the plane $x = 0$ but extending infinitely in all other directions. Suppose that initially it is at zero temperature (equation (2)) and that the face $x = 0$ is brought to a constant temperature U_0 and held there for $t > 0$ (equation (3)). Then the temperature $U(x, t)$ in the solid depends only upon the distance x from the plane $x = 0$ and the time t and satisfies the equation (1) under certain fairly general conditions. The coefficient a is called the thermal diffusivity of the material and is equal to $k/c\rho$, where k is the thermal conductivity, c is the specific heat per unit mass, and ρ is the density of the material. Equation (4) expresses the fact that at any given time the temperature of a point at a great distance from the heated face is still zero, that is, the heat has not yet reached this point.

The solution of this problem is now straightforward.   Let us take the transform of (1) and use (2) to get

(5) $$\frac{d^2u(x, s)}{dx^2} - \frac{s}{a} u(x, s) = 0,$$

where $u(x, s) = L_t\{U(x, t)\}$.   The general solution of this ordinary differential equation is

(6) $$u(x, s) = A(s)e^{+x\sqrt{\frac{s}{a}}} + B(s)e^{-x\sqrt{\frac{s}{a}}}.$$

This function must satisfy the transforms of the conditions (3) and (4), that is, with $s > 0$,

(7) $$u(0, s) = \frac{U_0}{s}, \quad \lim_{x \to \infty} u(x, s) = 0.$$

The second of these conditions implies that $A(s) = 0$ if the solution $u(x, s)$ given by (6) is to remain finite.   The condition at $x = 0$ gives $B(s) = \dfrac{U_0}{s}$, and therefore the solution of (5) and (7) is

(8) $$u(x, s) = \frac{U_0}{s} e^{-x\sqrt{\frac{s}{a}}}.$$

The inverse transform is given by

(9) $$U(x, t) = U_0\left[1 - \text{erf}\left(\frac{x}{2\sqrt{at}}\right)\right],$$

where

$$\text{erf}(z) = \frac{2}{\sqrt{\pi}} \int_0^z e^{-y^2} \, dy. \quad \text{(See Chapter 6, Exercises 3, 3.)}$$

The function given by (9) represents a formal solution of the problem given by (1), (2), (3), and (4) and therefore it is required that we show that it is in fact the solution we seek.   In order to do this, we write the solution in the more explicit form

(10) $$U(x, t) = U_0\left[1 - \frac{2}{\sqrt{\pi}} \int_0^{\frac{x}{2\sqrt{at}}} e^{-y^2} dy\right].$$

Differentiation of $U(x, t)$ with respect to t gives

$$\frac{\partial U(x, t)}{\partial t} = -\frac{2U_0}{\sqrt{\pi}} e^{-\frac{x^2}{4at}} \frac{d}{dt}\left(\frac{x}{2\sqrt{at}}\right) = \frac{U_0 x}{2t\sqrt{\pi at}} e^{-\frac{x^2}{4at}}.$$

Further,

$$\frac{\partial U(x, t)}{\partial x} = -\frac{2U_0}{\sqrt{\pi}} e^{-\frac{x^2}{4at}} \frac{d}{dx}\left(\frac{x}{2\sqrt{at}}\right) = -\frac{U_0}{\sqrt{\pi at}} e^{-\frac{x^2}{4at}},$$

$$\frac{\partial^2 U(x, t)}{\partial^2 x} = -\frac{U_0}{\sqrt{\pi at}} e^{-\frac{x^2}{4at}}\left(-\frac{x}{2at}\right) = \frac{U_0 x}{2at\sqrt{\pi at}} e^{-\frac{x^2}{4at}}.$$

From these derivatives it is clear that (1) is satisfied by our solution function $U(x, t)$. If we let $t \to 0$ in (10) we get

$$U(x, 0) = U_0\left[1 - \frac{2}{\sqrt{\pi}} \int_0^\infty e^{-y^2}\, dy\right]$$

and since $\int_0^\infty e^{-y^2}\, dy = \frac{\sqrt{\pi}}{2}$ (see §1.2, Example 3), it is clear that condition (2) is satisfied. For $x = 0$, $U(x, t)$ reduces to U_0 because upon substitution of $x = 0$ into (10) the range of the integral is reduced to zero. Finally since

$$\lim_{x \to \infty} U(x, t) = U_0\left[1 - \frac{2}{\sqrt{\pi}} \lim_{x \to \infty} \int_0^{\frac{x}{2\sqrt{at}}} e^{-y^2}\, dy\right]$$

$$= U_0\left[1 - \frac{2}{\sqrt{\pi}} \int_0^\infty e^{-y^2}\, dy\right]$$

$$= 0,$$

we see that (4) is also satisfied and that the function $U(x, t)$ given by (9) is indeed the solution of our problem.

EXERCISES 4

1. Solve the heat equation

$$\frac{\partial U(x, t)}{\partial t} = a\frac{\partial^2 U(x, t)}{\partial x^2}, \qquad (x > 0, t \geq 0)$$

subject to the following conditions:

(a) $U(x, 0) = U_1$, a constant, $(x > 0)$,

   $U(0, t) = U_0 > U_1$, $(t > 0)$,

   $\lim_{x \to \infty} U(x, t) = U_1$, $(t \geq 0)$.

(b) $U(x, 0) = U_1 x$, $(x > 0)$,

   $U(0, t) = U_0$, $(t > 0)$,

   $\lim_{x \to \infty} \dfrac{U(x, t)}{x} = U_1$, $(t \geq 0)$.

(c) $U(x, 0) = U_1$, $(x > 0)$,

   $U(0, t) = U_0 t$, $(t > 0)$,

   $\lim_{x \to \infty} U(x, t) = U_1$, $(t \geq 0)$.

2. Suppose that two semi-infinite solids having different thermal conductivities abut along the plane $x = 0$. Then the heat transfer across this boundary obeys the conditions

$$U(0^-, t) = U(0^+, t),$$

$$a_1 \frac{\partial U(0^-, t)}{\partial x} = a_2 \frac{\partial U(0^+, t)}{\partial x},$$

where U is the temperature distribution and a_1 and a_2 are the thermal diffusivities for the regions R_1 $(x < 0)$ and R_2 $(x > 0)$ respectively. The functions $U(x, t)$ satisfy the equations

$$\frac{\partial U(x, t)}{\partial t} = a_1 \frac{\partial^2 U(x, t)}{\partial x^2}, \qquad (x < 0, t \geq 0),$$

$$\frac{\partial U(x, t)}{\partial t} = a_2 \frac{\partial^2 U(x, t)}{\partial x^2}, \qquad (x > 0, t \geq 0).$$

Suppose that the two semi-infinite solids are initially at constant temperatures A_1, $(-\infty < x < 0)$ and A_2, $(0 < x < \infty)$ and subject to the boundary conditions

$$\lim_{x \to -\infty} \frac{\partial U(x, t)}{\partial x} = 0,$$

$$\lim_{x \to +\infty} \frac{\partial U(x, t)}{\partial x} = 0.$$

Determine the temperature distribution in these regions.

5.7 TEMPERATURE DISTRIBUTION IN A BAR OF FINITE LENGTH

Suppose that the bar shown in Fig. 49 is homogeneous and has its lateral surfaces insulated to prevent the flow of heat through them.

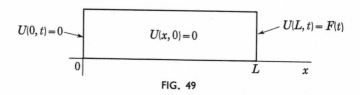

FIG. 49

We wish to determine the temperature $U(x, t)$ in the bar under the conditions that the bar is initially at zero temperature and that the end at $x = 0$ is held at zero temperature for all $t \geq 0$. However, the temperature at the other end is some specified function of t. Then our boundary value problem is

$$(1) \qquad \frac{\partial U(x, t)}{\partial t} = a \frac{\partial^2 U(x, t)}{\partial x^2}, \qquad (t \geq 0, 0 \leq x \leq L),$$

$$(2) \qquad U(x, 0) = 0, \qquad (0 \leq x < L),$$

$$(3) \qquad U(0, t) = 0, \quad U(L, t) = F(t), \qquad (t \geq 0).$$

The transformed problem is

$$(4) \qquad su(x, s) = a \frac{d^2 u(x, s)}{dx^2},$$

$$(5) \qquad u(0, s) = 0, \quad u(L, s) = f(s),$$

and its solution is given by

(6) $$u(x, s) = f(s) \frac{\sinh \sqrt{\frac{s}{a}} x}{\sinh \sqrt{\frac{s}{a}} L}.$$

If we observe that

(7) $$\frac{\sinh \alpha}{\sinh \beta} = \frac{e^{\alpha} - e^{-\alpha}}{e^{\beta} - e^{-\beta}} = e^{-\beta} \frac{e^{\alpha} - e^{-\alpha}}{1 - e^{-2\beta}}$$

$$= [e^{-(\beta - \alpha)} - e^{-(\beta + \alpha)}] \frac{1}{1 - e^{-2\beta}}$$

$$= [e^{-(\beta - \alpha)} - e^{-(\beta + \alpha)}] \sum_{k=0}^{\infty} e^{-2k\beta}$$

$$= \sum_{k=0}^{\infty} [e^{-[(2k+1)\beta - \alpha]} - e^{-[(2k+1)\beta + \alpha]}],$$

we may write the solution of the transformed problem in the form

(8) $$u(x, s) = f(s) \sum_{k=0}^{\infty} \left[e^{-[(2k+1)L - x]\sqrt{\frac{s}{a}}} - e^{-[(2k+1)L + x]\sqrt{\frac{s}{a}}} \right].$$

Now if we make use of the Convolution Theorem, we find that for $(2k + 1)L - x > 0$,

$$L^{-1} \left\{ f(s) e^{-[(2k+1)L - x]\sqrt{\frac{s}{a}}} \right\}$$

$$= \int_0^t F(t - \lambda) \frac{(2k + 1)L - x}{2\sqrt{\pi a \lambda^3}} e^{-\frac{[(2k+1)L - x]^2}{4a\lambda}} d\lambda.$$

Thus if we set

$$\frac{(2k + 1)L - x}{2\sqrt{a\lambda}} = z,$$

then

$$\lambda = \frac{[(2k + 1)L - x]^2}{4az^2},$$

and

$$-\frac{1}{2} \frac{(2k + 1)L - x}{2\sqrt{a\lambda^3}} d\lambda = dz.$$

Hence we may write

$$L^{-1}\left\{f(s)e^{-[(2k+1)L-x]\sqrt{\frac{s}{a}}}\right\}$$

$$= \frac{-2}{\sqrt{\pi}} \int_{\infty}^{\frac{(2k+1)L-x}{2\sqrt{at}}} F\left(t - \frac{[(2k+1)L-x]^2}{4az^2}\right)e^{-z^2}\,dz$$

$$= \frac{2}{\sqrt{\pi}} \int_{\frac{2(k+1)L-x}{2\sqrt{at}}}^{\infty} F\left(t - \frac{[(2k+1)L-x]^2}{4az^2}\right)e^{-z^2}\,dz$$

$$= \frac{2}{\sqrt{\pi}} \int_{0}^{\infty} F\left(t - \frac{[(2k+1)L-x]^2}{4az^2}\right)$$

$$\times \mathscr{U}\left(t - \frac{[(2k+1)L-x]^2}{4az^2}\right)e^{-z^2}\,dz.$$

Thus the formal solution of our problem is given by

(9) $U(x, t) = L^{-1}\{u(x, s)\}$

$$= \frac{2}{\sqrt{\pi}} \sum_{k=0}^{\infty} \left\{ \int_{0}^{\infty} F\left(t - \frac{[(2k+1)L-x]^2}{4az^2}\right) \right.$$

$$\times \mathscr{U}\left(t - \frac{[(2k+1)L-x]^2}{4az^2}\right)e^{-z^2}\,dz$$

$$- \int_{0}^{\infty} F\left(t - \frac{[(2k+1)L+x]^2}{4az^2}\right)$$

$$\left. \times \mathscr{U}\left(t - \frac{[(2k+1)L+x]^2}{4az^2}\right)e^{-z^2}\,dz\right\}.$$

We shall not verify this formula here, since a complete discussion would be somewhat lengthy. We content ourselves by considering a special case in which the end $x = L$ is kept at a constant temperature F_0.   Then (9) reduces to

$$(10) \quad U(x, t) = \frac{2F_0}{\sqrt{\pi}} \sum_{k=0}^{\infty} \left\{ \int_0^{\infty} \mathscr{U}\left(t - \frac{[(2k+1)L - x]^2}{4az^2}\right) e^{-z^2} \, dz \right.$$

$$- \left. \int_0^{\infty} \mathscr{U}\left(t - \frac{[(2k+1)L + x]^2}{4az^2}\right) e^{-z^2} \, dz \right\}$$

$$= F_0 \sum_{k=0}^{\infty} \left\{ \operatorname{erf}\left(\frac{(2k+1)L + x}{2\sqrt{at}}\right) \right.$$

$$- \left. \operatorname{erf}\left(\frac{(2k+1)L - x}{2\sqrt{at}}\right) \right\}.$$

The verification that (10) does in fact give a solution of the problem in the special case of $F(t) = F_0$ is not difficult if we note that

$$U(L, t) = F_0 \sum_{k=0}^{\infty} \left\{ \operatorname{erf}\left(\frac{(k+1)}{\sqrt{at}} L\right) - \operatorname{erf}\left(\frac{kL}{\sqrt{at}}\right) \right\}$$

$$= \frac{2F_0}{\sqrt{\pi}} \sum_{k=0}^{\infty} \int_{\frac{kL}{\sqrt{at}}}^{\frac{k+1}{\sqrt{at}} L} e^{-z^2} \, dz = \frac{2F_0}{\sqrt{\pi}} \int_0^{\infty} e^{-z^2} \, dz = F_0.$$

The student should check that the remaining conditions of the problem are satisfied by $U(x, t)$ as given by (10).

EXERCISES 5

1.   Suppose that an insulated bar is brought to a uniform temperature U_0, and then the end at $x = 0$ is insulated and the temperature at the end at $x = L$ is reduced to zero.   Find the temperature distribution in the bar for all $t \geq 0$ and $0 \leq x < L$.   [Note: the fact that the end $x = 0$ is insulated means that there is no loss of heat through that end, that is, $\dfrac{\partial U(0, t)}{\partial x} = 0$, $(t > 0)$.]

2.   If heat is generated at the rate of $c\rho F(t)$ per unit length in a bar, then equation (1) must be changed to read

$$\frac{\partial U(x, t)}{\partial t} = a \frac{\partial^2 U(x, t)}{\partial x^2} + F(t).$$

Now suppose that the initial temperature in a bar of length L is zero and that the end $x = L$ is kept at zero for all $t \geq 0$. Let the end $x = 0$ and the lateral surface be insulated. Determine the temperature distribution in the bar if $F(t) = F_0$.

3. Take $F(t) = 1$, $(0 \leq t < t_0)$,

$$= 0, \quad (t \geq t_0),$$

in 2 and find the temperature distribution in the bar.

4. Let a bar of length L be at temperature zero initially and let both ends be brought to a constant temperature U_0. Find the temperature distribution in the bar.

5.8 THE TELEGRAPH EQUATIONS

As our final example in partial differential equations, we consider the flow of electricity in a transmission line. The basic differential equations are

$$(1) \quad \frac{\partial^2 V(x, t)}{\partial x^2} = LC \frac{\partial^2 V(x, t)}{\partial t^2} + (RC + GL) \frac{\partial V(x, t)}{\partial t} + RGV(x, t),$$

and a similar one obtained by replacing $V(x, t)$ by $I(x, t)$. Here V and I represent the potential and current, respectively, at any point x along the line at any time t. The quantities R, L, G, and C are known as line constants and represent the resistance, inductance. conductance to ground, and capacitance to ground, respectively, per unit length of the line. The differential equations in V and I are known as the telephone equations. In practice it is sometimes found that some of the constants R, L, G, and C may be neglected, thereby simplifying the equations. In particular, in telegraph transmission the leakage G and inductance L are so small that they may be neglected so that the original equation (1), and its analog for I reduce to

$$(2) \quad \begin{aligned} \frac{\partial^2 V}{\partial x^2} &= RC \frac{\partial V}{\partial t}, \\ \frac{\partial^2 I}{\partial x^2} &= RC \frac{\partial I}{\partial t}. \end{aligned}$$

These equations are known as the *telegraph equations*. It should be observed that these equations have the same form as the heat equation (1), §5.6 with $a = \dfrac{1}{RC}$, and therefore the flow of current in this instance is analogous to the flow of heat discussed in §5.6. Therefore we may utilize the results of §5.6 to obtain information about the potential or current in a telegraph line.   To illustrate this we consider the following two examples.

Example 1. Suppose that the potential in a semi-infinite telegraph line is initially zero and at time $t = 0$ a constant voltage V_0 is applied at the end $x = 0$. Then the potential function $V(x, t)$ satisfies the equation

$$\frac{\partial^2 V}{\partial x^2} = RC \frac{\partial V}{\partial t} \qquad (t \geq 0, x > 0)$$

and the conditions

$$V(x, 0) = 0, \qquad (x > 0),$$

$$V(0, t) = V_0, \qquad (t > 0),$$

$$\lim_{x \to \infty} V(x, t) = 0, \qquad (t \geq 0).$$

Comparison of this problem with that of §5.6 shows that it is mathematically the same problem and therefore we may conclude that the solution is

$$V(x, t) = V_0 \left[1 - \operatorname{erf} \left(\frac{x}{2} \sqrt{\frac{RC}{t}} \right) \right].$$

Example 2. Suppose that a transmission line of length L is grounded at the end $x = 0$ and has an alternating voltage $E_0 \cos \omega t$ applied at the end $x = L$.   Under the assumption that the line has a zero initial potential, find the voltage $V(x, t)$ for $t \geq 0, 0 \leq x < L$.

The potential V satisfies the following system:

$$\frac{\partial^2 V}{\partial x^2} = RC \frac{\partial V}{\partial t}, \qquad (0 \leq x < L, t \geq 0),$$

$$V(x, 0) = 0 \qquad 0 \leq x < L.$$

$$V(0, t) = 0, \qquad V(L, t) = E_0 \cos \omega t, \qquad t \geq 0.$$

Again, this problem is equivalent to a previous one, that of §5.7;

so we need only replace $F(t)$ in (9), §5.7 by $E_0 \cos \omega t$ and proceed from there to obtain the solution of this problem.

Another interesting case of (1) arises if the resistance R and the conductance G are small enough to be neglected. In this case the telephone equations reduce to

(3)
$$\frac{\partial^2 V}{\partial x^2} = LC \frac{\partial^2 V}{\partial t^2},$$

$$\frac{\partial^2 I}{\partial x^2} = LC \frac{\partial^2 I}{\partial t^2}.$$

These equations are also those which are usually applicable at high frequencies. For at high frequencies, the factor arising from time differentiation is large and therefore the terms involving I and $\frac{\partial I}{\partial t}$ are small in comparison with $\frac{\partial^2 I}{\partial t^2}$, and similarly for V. Thus by neglecting the terms in I and $\frac{\partial I}{\partial t}$ we get equations (3). Now equations (3) are examples of one-dimensional wave equations, and therefore the information obtained in §§5.3, 5.4 may be useful in the solution of the problems associated with certain types of transmission lines.

Finally, we shall discuss the case of the telephone equation in which the inductance L is negligible. In this instance equation (1) reduces to

(4)
$$\frac{\partial^2 V}{\partial x^2} - RC \frac{\partial V}{\partial t} - RGV = 0.$$

A problem illustrating this case is given in the following example.

Example 3. Suppose that we are concerned with a semi-infinite insulated line which has a constant initial potential V_0. At time $t = 0$ let the end $x = 0$ be grounded and let us find V for any $t > 0$.

Then the boundary conditions to be associated with equation (4) are

(5)
$$V(x, 0) = V_0, \qquad (x > 0),$$

(6)
$$V(0, t) = 0, \quad \lim_{x \to \infty} \frac{\partial V(x, t)}{\partial x} = 0, \qquad (t > 0).$$

The last condition of (6) implies that the current at a great distance down the line is zero.   The transformed problem is

(7) $$\frac{d^2v(x, s)}{dx^2} - RC(sv(x, s) - V_0) - RGv(x, s) = 0,$$

(8) $$v(0, s) = 0, \quad \lim_{x \to \infty} \frac{dv(x, s)}{dx} = 0.$$

Equation (7) may be written in the more conventional form

(7a) $$\frac{d^2v}{dx^2} - (RCs + RG)v = -RCV_0$$

from which we see that the general solution is

(9) $$v(x, s) = A(s)e^{x\sqrt{RCs + RG}} + B(s)e^{-x\sqrt{RCs + RG}} + \frac{CV_0}{Cs + G}.$$

The second condition of (8) requires that $A = 0$ and the first gives $B = -\dfrac{CV_0}{Cs + G}.$ Hence

(10) $$v(x, s) = \frac{CV_0}{Cs + G}(1 - e^{-x\sqrt{RCs + RG}}).$$

Therefore, we have

(11) $$V(x, t) = L^{-1}\{v(x, s)\} = V_0 e^{-\frac{G}{C}t}\, \text{erf}\left(\frac{x}{2\sqrt{\,}}\sqrt{\frac{RC}{t}}\right).$$

EXERCISES 6

1.   Let a constant potential V_0 be impressed on a semi-infinite telegraph line at $x = 0$ and assume that the initial potential of the line is V_1.   Find the potential $V(x, t)$ for all $t > 0$, $x > 0$.

2.   Let the line in 1 be of a finite length L and let it be grounded at $x = L$, otherwise the remaining conditions of 1 hold.   Find the potential in this line.

3.   A line initially at zero potential is grounded at $x = L$ and an alternating voltage $V_0 \sin 3t$ is applied to the end $x = 0$ at $t = 0$.   Find $V(x, t)$ for $t > 0$, $0 < x < L$.

4. Solve the following boundary value problem:

$$\frac{\partial^2 V}{\partial x^2} - A \frac{\partial V}{\partial t} - BV = 0, \qquad (x > 0, \quad t \ge 0),$$

$$V(x, 0) = V_0, \qquad (x > 0),$$

$$V(0, t) = V_1[\mathscr{U}(t) - \mathscr{U}(t - t_0)], \qquad (t > 0),$$

$$\lim_{x \to \infty} \frac{\partial V(x, t)}{\partial x} = 0, \qquad (t \ge 0).$$

5. If a transmission line is initially dead, that is, there is no current or voltage and no change of current and voltage with respect to t in the line, then the potential $V(x, t)$ satisfies the equation $\frac{\partial^2 V}{\partial x^2} = LC \frac{\partial^2 V}{\partial t^2}$. At $t = 0$ a potential $F(t)$ is impressed at the end $x = 0$ and the far end is left open. Then the boundary conditions are $V(x, 0) = \frac{\partial V(x, 0)}{\partial t} = 0$, $(x > 0)$, $V(0, t) = F(t)$, $(t > 0)$ and $\lim_{x \to \infty} \frac{\partial V(x, t)}{\partial x} = 0$, $(t \ge 0)$. Find $V(x, t)$ for all $t \ge 0$, $x > 0$.

6. Solve 5 for the cases

    (a) $F(t) \equiv 1$,   (b) $F(t) \equiv t$,   (c) $F(t) \equiv \sin \omega t$.

6

Transforms of Functions with Infinite Discontinuities

+++

6.1 INTRODUCTION

We have seen that the Laplace transform of a function can exist even though the function is not of class T (for instance, Example 3, §1.2, and Example 3, §2.2). The former example belongs to a larger class of functions whose transforms are needed for some applications such as we have already encountered in Chapter 5. This larger class of functions, which we shall call *class T_α*, differs from class T at most in behavior at $t = 0$. A function $F(t)$ is defined to be of class T_α if

(*a*) $F(t)$ is of exponential order e^{at} for some a and has at most a finite number of discontinuities in the interval $0 \leq t \leq b$ for all $b > 0$, those occurring in $0 < t \leq b$ being finite, and

(*b*) $F(t)$ may have an *infinite discontinuity* at $t = 0$ *of order $t^{-\alpha}$*, for some α $(0 < \alpha < 1)$, as defined below. Otherwise $F(0^+)$ is finite.†

A function $F(t)$ is said to have an *infinite discontinuity of* order $t^{-\alpha}$, $(0 < \alpha < 1)$, at $t = 0$ if $F(t)$ is unbounded as $t \to 0^+$, but for the given α there exist constants $M > 0$ and $t_0 > 0$ such that

$$\left| t^\alpha F(t) \right| \leq M, \qquad (0 < t < t_0).$$

Note that if $F(t)$ is of order $t^{-\alpha}$ at $t = 0$, then for any $\varepsilon > 0$ and for $0 < t < t_0 < 1$, $\left| t^{\alpha + \varepsilon} F(t) \right| < \left| t^\alpha F(t) \right| \leq M$. Hence if $F(t)$ is of

---

† If $F(t)$ is of class T, then it also belongs to class T_α for every α in the range $0 < \alpha < 1$.

order $t^{-\alpha}$ at $t = 0$, it is also of order $t^{-(\alpha+\varepsilon)}$ where ε is such that $\alpha + \varepsilon < 1$.

Example 1. In §1.2 we proved directly that t^{α}, $(\alpha > -1)$, has a transform. It is clear that this function is of class $T_{-\alpha}$ for $-1 < \alpha < 0$.

Example 2. The function $F(t) = t^{-1/2}e^t$ is of class $T_{1/2}$. For, $t^{1/2}(t^{-1/2}e^t) = e^t < e$ if $0 < t < 1$. Also $t^{-1/2}e^t \le e^t$ for $t \ge 1$, hence the function is of exponential order e^t. Note that $F(t)$ is therefore of class $T_{\frac{1}{2}+\varepsilon}$, where $\frac{1}{2} + \varepsilon < 1$, $\varepsilon > 0$.

Example 3. The function $\ln t$ is of class T_{α}, for every α in the range $0 < \alpha < 1$. For if we let $t \to 0^+$ then $t^{\alpha} \ln t \to 0$. (See 2 in Exercises 1, below.) Furthermore, $\ln t < e^t$ for $t > 0$.

EXERCISES I

1. Sketch $F(t)$ of Example 2. Also sketch, on same graph, e^t, $t^{-1/2}$, and $et^{-1/2}$.

2. If $F(t)$ has an infinite discontinuity at $t = 0$ and if $\lim\limits_{t\to0^+} t^{\alpha'}F(t) = 0$, for some α' such that $0 < \alpha' < 1$, show that $F(t)$ is of order $t^{-\alpha'}$ at $t = 0$. (Alternatively we may require $\lim\limits_{t\to0^+} t^{\alpha'}F(t)$ exists.)

3. Which of the following functions are of class T_{α}?

(a) $\dfrac{\cosh t}{\sqrt{t}}$.   (c) $F(t) = \begin{cases} t^{-3/4}, & (0 < t < 2), \\ e^t, & (t \ge 2). \end{cases}$

(b) $\cosh t^2$.   (d) $\dfrac{\sin t}{\sqrt{t}}$.

6.2 EXTENSION OF EXISTENCE AND DERIVATIVE THEOREMS

In this section we shall sketch proofs of the following theorems, the first of which is an extension of Theorem IV, §2.2, and the second an extension of Theorem VI, §2.3.

Theorem XVI. *If $F(t)$ is a function of class T_{α}, then $L\{F(t)\}$ is absolutely convergent for $s > a$.*

Proof. If $F(t)$ has an infinite discontinuity of order $t^{-\alpha}$, $(0 < \alpha < 1)$, at $t = 0$, then it is necessary to modify equation (7), §2.2, to read

$$\int_0^\infty e^{-st}F(t)\,dt = \int_0^{t_1} e^{-st}F(t)\,dt + \int_{t_1}^\infty e^{-st}F(t)\,dt$$

$$= \int_0^{t_1} e^{-st}F(t)\,dt + \lim_{b \to \infty} \left[\int_{t_1}^{t_n} e^{-st}F(t)\,dt \right.$$

$$\left. + \int_{t_n}^b e^{-st}F(t)\,dt \right], \qquad (t_1 > 0).$$

The absolute convergence of the last limit follows as in §2.2, hence it remains to prove the absolute convergence of $\int_0^{t_1} e^{-st}F(t)\,dt$. From the assumed order property of $F(t)$ at $t = 0$, there exist positive constants α, M, t_0 such that

$$|F(t)| \le Mt^{-\alpha}, \qquad (0 < \alpha < 1, \ 0 < t \le t_0 < t_1).$$

Now choose a number ε, $(0 < \varepsilon < t_0)$, and write

$$\int_0^{t_1} e^{-st}|F(t)|\,dt = \lim_{\varepsilon \to 0^+} \int_\varepsilon^{t_0} e^{-st}|F(t)|\,dt + \int_{t_0}^{t_1} e^{-st}|F(t)|\,dt.$$

The last integral exists because $F(t)$ is sectionally continuous in the interval $t_0 \le t \le t_1$. Now $0 < e^{-st} < 1$ for $s > 0$, $t > 0$, and making use of the bound on $|F(t)|$ we have $e^{-st}|F(t)| \le Mt^{-\alpha}$, $(0 < t \le t_0)$. Thus

$$\int_\varepsilon^{t_0} e^{-st}|F(t)|\,dt \le \int_\varepsilon^{t_0} Mt^{-\alpha}\,dt = \frac{M}{1-\alpha}\,t^{1-\alpha}\Big|_\varepsilon^{t_0}$$

$$= \frac{M}{1-\alpha}\,[t_0^{1-\alpha} - \varepsilon^{1-\alpha}].$$

Hence

$$\int_0^{t_0} e^{-st}|F(t)|\,dt = \lim_{\varepsilon \to 0^+} \int_\varepsilon^{t_0} e^{-st}|F(t)|\,dt \le \frac{M}{1-\alpha}\,t_0^{1-\alpha},$$

which shows that $\int_0^{t_0} e^{-st}F(t)\,dt$ is absolutely convergent. This fact coupled with the existence of $\int_{t_0}^{t_1} e^{-st}F(t)\,dt$ proves that $\int_0^{t_1} e^{-st}F(t)\,dt$ is absolutely convergent.

Theorem XVII. *Let*

(1) $F(t)$ *be of class T with at most a finite number of discontinuities,*

(2) $F'(t)$ *be sectionally continuous except that $F'(0^+)$ need not exist. Then if $t_1, \cdots, t_n$ are the positive abscissas of the points of discontinuity of $F(t)$,*

$$L\{F'(t)\} = sL\{F(t)\} - F(0^+) - \sum_{i=1}^{n} e^{-st_i}[F(t_i^+) - F(t_i^-)], \quad (s > a).$$

Proof. The proof of Theorem VI, §2.3, must be modified as follows: Under the conditions above, the definition of $L\{F'(t)\}$ must be taken as

$$L\{F'(t)\} = \lim_{\substack{\varepsilon \to 0^+ \\ b \to \infty}} \int_{\varepsilon}^{b} e^{-st} F'(t) \, dt.$$

Now, if $\tau_1, \cdots, \tau_m$ are the positive abscissas of the points of discontinuity of $F'(t)$ between 0 and b, then we may write

$$\int_{\varepsilon}^{b} e^{-st} F'(t) \, dt = \int_{\varepsilon}^{\tau_1} e^{-st} F'(t) \, dt$$
$$+ \sum_{i=1}^{m-1} \int_{\tau_i}^{\tau_{i+1}} e^{-st} F'(t) \, dt + \int_{\tau_m}^{b} e^{-st} F'(t) \, dt.$$

Then integration by parts gives

$$\int_{\varepsilon}^{b} e^{-st} F'(t) \, dt = -e^{-s\varepsilon} F(\varepsilon) + e^{-sb} F(b^-) + s \int_{\varepsilon}^{b} e^{-st} F(t) \, dt$$
$$- \sum_{i=1}^{m} e^{-s\tau_i}[F(\tau_i^+) - F(\tau_i^-)].$$

Now as $\varepsilon \to 0^+$ and $b \to \infty$ we get the desired result by following an argument analogous to that used to complete the proof of Theorem VI, §2.3.

EXERCISES 2

1. Use Theorem I, §1.3 to show that

$$L\{t^{-1/2}e^t\} = \left(\frac{\pi}{s-1}\right)^{1/2}.$$

2. Show that

$$L\{\ln t\} = \frac{1}{s}\,\Gamma'(1) - \frac{\ln s}{s}.$$

[Use the substitution $u = st$.   Note that

$$\Gamma'(x) = \int_0^\infty t^{x-1}e^{-t}\ln t\,dt.]$$

3. Given that

$$L\{\sin 2\sqrt{t}\} = \left(\frac{\pi}{s^3}\right)^{1/2}e^{-1/s},$$

show that

$$L\left\{\frac{\cos 2\sqrt{t}}{\sqrt{t}}\right\} = \left(\frac{\pi}{s}\right)^{1/2}e^{-1/s}.$$

4. Find $L\{t\ln t\}$.

6.3 EXTENSION OF THE CONVOLUTION THEOREM

We shall assume the following lemma without proof.

Lemma.   *Let $F(t)$ be of class T_α and $G(t)$ of class T_β.   Then $F * G$ is of class T_γ for $\gamma = \alpha + \beta - 1$ and $F * G$ is continuous for $t > 0$. (If $\gamma \leqslant 0$, then $F * G$ is of class T.)*

The proof can be based on the fact† that if $\phi(x)$ is a properly integrable function on $a \leqslant x \leqslant b$, and $a < h < k < b$, then

$$\int_h^k |\phi(x + \delta) - \phi(x)|\,dx \to 0$$

as $\delta \to 0$.

We may now consider the extension of the Convolution Theorem to class T_α functions.   If $F(t)$ and $G(t)$ are of class T_{α_1} and class T_{α_2}, respectively, then care must be taken to be certain

---

† G. Doetsch, *Theorie und Anwendung der Laplace-Transformation* (Berlin, Springer, 1937), pp. 399–400.

that the interchange of the order of integration (such as that done to obtain (5), §2.4) is legitimate. The convolution integral is defined by

$$\int_0^t F(x)G(t-x)\,dx = \lim_{\substack{\varepsilon\to 0^+ \\ \delta\to 0^+}} \int_\delta^{t-\varepsilon} F(x)G(t-x)\,dx.$$

Thus, it is necessary to replace (4), §2.4, by

$$L\{F*G\} = \lim_{\substack{K\to\infty \\ \varepsilon\to 0^+ \\ \delta\to 0^+}} \int_{\varepsilon+\delta}^{2K} e^{-st}\left(\int_\delta^{t-\varepsilon} F(x)G(t-x)'dx\right)dt,$$

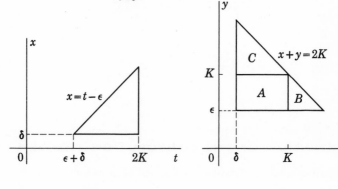

FIG. 50   FIG. 51

where the region of integration is shown in Fig. 50 (compare with Fig. 7). Within such a region, the interchange is permissible because the integrand $e^{-st}F(x)G(t-x)$ is continuous except on a set of zero area.† Hence we have

$$\int_{\varepsilon+\delta}^{2K} e^{-st}\,dt \int_\delta^{t-\varepsilon} F(x)G(t-x)\,dx = \int_\delta^{2K-\varepsilon} F(x)\,dx \int_{x+\varepsilon}^{2K} e^{-st}G(t-x)\,dt$$

$$= \int_\delta^{2K-\varepsilon} e^{-sx}F(x)\,dx \int_\varepsilon^{2K-x} e^{-sy}G(y)\,dy.$$

The last equality is obtained by changing the variable of integration from t to $y = t - x$, which changes the region of integration into the

† R. C. Buck, *Advanced Calculus* (New York, McGraw-Hill, 1956), p. 65.

one pictured in Fig. 51 (compare with Fig. 6).   Again if we designate
this last integral by $I(R)$, we have

$$I(R) = \int_\delta^{2K-\varepsilon} e^{-sx} F(x)\, dx \int_\varepsilon^{2K-x} e^{-sy} G(y)\, dy = \int\int_R e^{-s(x+y)} F(x) G(y)\, dx\, dy$$

$$= \int\int_{A+B+C} e^{-s(x+y)} F(x) G(y)\, dx\, dy = I(A) + I(B) + I(C).$$

Thus if we show that $\lim I(B) = \lim I(C) = 0$ as $\varepsilon \to 0^+$, $\delta \to 0^+$,
and $K \to \infty$, we will have

$$L\{F * G\} = \lim_{\substack{\varepsilon \to 0^+ \\ \delta \to 0^+ \\ K \to \infty}} I(R) = \lim_{\substack{\varepsilon \to 0^+ \\ \delta \to 0^+ \\ K \to \infty}} I(A) = \lim_{\substack{\varepsilon \to 0^+ \\ \delta \to 0^+ \\ K \to \infty}} \int\int_A e^{-s(x+y)} F(x) G(y)\, dx\, dy$$

$$= \lim_{\substack{K \to \infty \\ \delta \to 0^+}} \int_\delta^K e^{-sx} F(x)\, dx \cdot \lim_{\substack{K \to \infty \\ \varepsilon \to 0^+}} \int_\varepsilon^K e^{-sy} G(y)\, dy = f(s)g(s).$$

To show that $\lim I(B) = 0$ as $K \to \infty$ and $\varepsilon \to 0^+$, we write

$$|I(B)| = \left| \int\int_B e^{-s(x+y)} F(x) G(y)\, dx\, dy \right|$$

$$\leq \int\int_B e^{-s(x+y)} |(F(x)|\, |G(y)|\, dx\, dy$$

$$= \int_\varepsilon^K e^{-sy} |G(y)|\, dy \int_K^{2K-y} e^{-sx} |F(x)|\, dx$$

$$\leq \int_\varepsilon^K e^{-sy} |G(y)|\, dy \int_K^{2K} e^{-sx} |F(x)|\, dx.$$

Again, the convergence of $\int_0^\infty e^{-sx} |F(x)|\, dx$ (which implies that
$\int_K^{2K} e^{-sx} |F(x)|\, dx \to 0$ as $K \to \infty$) and the existence of $L\{|G(y)|\}$ imply
that $\lim_{\substack{K \to \infty \\ \varepsilon \to 0^+}} I(B) = 0$.   A similar argument proves that $\lim_{\substack{K \to \infty \\ \delta \to 0^+}} I(C) = 0$.

EXERCISES 3

1. Show that

$$L^{-1}\left\{\frac{1}{\sqrt{s}(s-1)}\right\} = \frac{e^t}{\sqrt{\pi}} \int_0^t \frac{e^{-\tau}}{\sqrt{\tau}} d\tau.$$

2. The "error function" erf (t), is defined by

$$\text{erf}(t) = \frac{2}{\sqrt{\pi}} \int_0^t e^{-x^2} dx.$$

Of importance in applications is

$$\text{erf}(\sqrt{t}) = \frac{2}{\sqrt{\pi}} \int_0^{\sqrt{t}} e^{-x^2} dx$$

$$= \frac{1}{\sqrt{\pi}} \int_0^t \tau^{-1/2} e^{-\tau} d\tau.$$

Derive the last integral by the substitution $\tau = x^2$. Show that

$$\text{erf}(\sqrt{t}) = 1 * (\pi t)^{-1/2} e^{-t}$$

and that

$$L\{\text{erf}\sqrt{t}\} = \frac{1}{s\sqrt{s-1}}.$$

3. Find the Laplace transform of $F(t) = \dfrac{e^{-\frac{k^2}{4t}}}{t^{3/2}}$ from the definition of the transform as follows:

(*a*) Show that

$$f(s) = \frac{4}{k} e^{-k\sqrt{s}} \int_0^\infty e^{-\left(\lambda - \frac{k\sqrt{s}}{2\lambda}\right)^2} d\lambda,$$

where $\lambda = k/(2\sqrt{t})$.

(*b*) Show that

$$\int_0^\infty e^{-\left(\lambda - \frac{c}{\lambda}\right)^2} d\lambda = \int_0^\infty \frac{c}{\mu^2} e^{-\left(\mu - \frac{c}{\mu}\right)^2} d\mu,$$

where $\mu = \dfrac{c}{\lambda}$, $c = \dfrac{k\sqrt{s}}{2}$.

(c)   Add and subtract 1 to the factor $\dfrac{c}{\mu^2}$ in step (b) to show that

$$\int_0^\infty e^{-\left(\lambda-\frac{c}{\lambda}\right)^2} d\lambda = \frac{1}{2} \int_{-\infty}^\infty e^{-x^2}\, dx = \frac{\sqrt{\pi}}{2},$$

where $x = \mu - \dfrac{c}{\mu}$.

(d)   Show that

$$L\{F(t)\} = \frac{2\sqrt{\pi}}{k}\, e^{-k\sqrt{s}}, \qquad (k > 0, \quad s > 0).$$

(e)   In step (d), divide by s and use the Convolution Theorem and the substitution $\tau = \dfrac{k^2}{4\sigma^2}$ to show that

$$L^{-1}\left\{\frac{1}{s}\, e^{-k\sqrt{s}}\right\} = 1 - \operatorname{erf}\left(\frac{k}{2\sqrt{t}}\right), \qquad (k > 0, \quad s > 0).$$

Bibliography

1. AGNEW, R. P., *Differential Equations* (New York, McGraw-Hill, 1942).
2. BUCK, R. C., *Advanced Calculus* (New York, McGraw-Hill, 1956).
3. CARSLAW, H. S., *Operational Methods in Applied Mathematics* (New York, Oxford University Press, 1942).
4. CHURCHILL, R. V., *Modern Operational Mathematics in Engineering* (New York, McGraw-Hill, 1944).
5. CODDINGTON, E. A., and LEVINSON, N., *Theory of Differential Equations* (New York, McGraw-Hill, 1955).
6. DOETSCH, G., *Theorie und Anwendung der Laplace-Transformation* (Springer, 1937).
7. GASKELL, R. E., *Engineering Mathematics* (New York, Dryden, 1958).
8. GRAVES, L. M., *The Theory of Functions of Real Variables* (New York, McGraw-Hill, 1946).
9. MACDUFFEE, C. C., *Theory of Equations* (New York, Wiley, 1954).
10. MCLACHLAN, N. W., *Modern Operational Calculus* (New York, Macmillan, 1948).
11. USPENSKY, J. V., *Theory of Equations* (New York, McGraw-Hill, 1948).
12. WIDDER, D. V., *Advanced Calculus* (Englewood Cliffs, N.J., Prentice-Hall, 1947).
13. WIDDER, D. V., *The Laplace Transform* (Princeton, N.J., Princeton University Press, 1946).
14. WYLIE, C. R., Jr., *Advanced Engineering Mathematics* (New York, McGraw-Hill, 1951).

Appendix I

Table of Operations

$F(t)$	$f(s)$	§
$F(t)$	$f(s) = \int_0^\infty e^{-st} F(t)\, dt$	1.2
$aF(t) + bG(t)$	$af(s) + bg(s)$	1.2
$e^{at} F(t)$	$f(s - a)$	1.3
$F(at)$	$\dfrac{1}{a} f\left(\dfrac{s}{a}\right)$	1.3
$F'(t)$	$sf(s) - F(0)$	1.5
$F^{(n)}(t)$	$s^n f(s) - s^{n-1}F(0) - s^{n-2}F'(0)$ $- \cdots - F^{(n-1)}(0)$	1.5
$F * G \equiv \displaystyle\int_0^t F(\tau)G(t - \tau)\, d\tau$	$f(s)g(s)$	2.4
$\displaystyle\int_0^t F(\tau)\, d\tau$	$\dfrac{1}{s} f(s)$	2.4
$t^n F(t),\ (n \text{ a positive integer})$	$(-1)^n \dfrac{d^n}{ds^n} f(s)$	2.6
$\dfrac{F(t)}{t}$	$\displaystyle\int_s^\infty f(x)\, dx$	2.7
$\mathcal{U}(t - a)F(t - a)$	$e^{-as} f(s)$	3.3
$F(t + T) = F(t)$	$\dfrac{1}{1 - e^{-sT}} \displaystyle\int_0^T e^{-st} F(t)\, dt$	3.5

Appendix II

Table of Transforms

F(t)	f(s)	§
1	$\dfrac{1}{s}$	1.2
t	$\dfrac{1}{s^2}$	1.2
t^α	$\dfrac{\Gamma(\alpha + 1)}{s^{\alpha+1}} \quad (\alpha > -1)$	1.2
$t^{-1/2}$	$\sqrt{\dfrac{\pi}{s}}$	1.2
$e^{\beta t}$	$\dfrac{1}{s - \beta}$	1.2
$\cos kt$	$\dfrac{s}{s^2 + k^2}$	1.2
$\sin kt$	$\dfrac{k}{s^2 + k^2}$	1.2
$\cosh kt$	$\dfrac{s}{s^2 - k^2}$	1.2
$\sinh kt$	$\dfrac{k}{s^2 - k^2}$	1.2

$F(t)$	$f(s)$	§
$e^{at} \cos kt$	$\dfrac{s-a}{(s-a)^2 + k^2}$	1.2
$e^{at} \sin kt$	$\dfrac{k}{(s-a)^2 + k^2}$	1.2
$e^{at}t^n$	$\dfrac{n!}{(s-a)^{n+1}}$	1.4
$t^n \cosh kt$	$\dfrac{n!}{2}\left[\dfrac{1}{(s-k)^{n+1}} + \dfrac{1}{(s+k)^{n+1}}\right]$	1.4
$t^n \sinh kt$	$\dfrac{n!}{2}\left[\dfrac{1}{(s-k)^{n+1}} - \dfrac{1}{(s+k)^{n+1}}\right]$	1.4
$\cosh^2 t$	$\dfrac{s^2 - 2}{s(s^2 - 4)}$	1.4
$\sinh^2 t$	$\dfrac{2}{s(s^2 - 4)}$	1.4
$t \cos kt$	$\dfrac{s^2 - k^2}{(s^2 + k^2)^2}$	1.5
$t \sin kt$	$\dfrac{2sk}{(s^2 + k^2)^2}$	1.5
$\sinh kt - \sin kt$	$\dfrac{2k^3}{s^4 - k^4}$	1.7
$\cosh kt - \cos kt$	$\dfrac{2k^2 s}{s^4 - k^4}$	1.7
$\sinh kt + \sin kt$	$\dfrac{2ks^2}{s^4 - k^4}$	1.7
$\cosh kt + \cos kt$	$\dfrac{2s^3}{s^4 - k^4}$	1.7

$F(t)$	$f(s)$	§
$1 - \cos kt$	$\dfrac{k^2}{s(s^2 + k^2)}$	2.4
$kt - \sin kt$	$\dfrac{k^3}{s^2(s^2 + k^2)}$	2.4
$\sin kt + kt \cos kt$	$\dfrac{2ks^2}{(s^2 + k^2)^2}$	2.4
$\sin kt - kt \cos kt$	$\dfrac{2k^3}{(s^2 + k^2)^2}$	2.4
$J_0(at)$	$\dfrac{1}{\sqrt{s^2 + a^2}}$	2.6
$\mathscr{U}(t - t_0)$	$\dfrac{e^{-st_0}}{s}$	3.2
$\mathscr{U}(t - a) - \mathscr{U}(t - b)$	$\dfrac{1}{s}(e^{-as} - e^{-bs})$	3.2
$\left[\mathscr{U}(t) - \mathscr{U}\left(t - \dfrac{\pi}{k}\right)\right] \sin kt$	$\dfrac{k}{s^2 + k^2}\left(1 + e^{-\frac{\pi s}{k}}\right)$	3.4
$\begin{aligned} F_p(t) &= \mathscr{U}(t)F(t) \\ &\quad - \mathscr{U}(t - T)F(t - T) \end{aligned}$	$\displaystyle\int_0^T e^{-st}F_p(t)\,dt$	3.5
Saw tooth function $F_p(t) = [\mathscr{U}(t) - \mathscr{U}(t - a)]\dfrac{t}{a}$ 	$f_p(s) = \dfrac{1 - e^{-as}}{as^2} - \dfrac{1}{s}e^{-as}$ $f(s) = \dfrac{1}{as^2} - \dfrac{e^{-as}}{s(1 - e^{-as})}$	3.5

$F(t)$	$f(s)$	§
Square-wave function $$F_p(t) = \mathscr{U}(t) - 2\mathscr{U}(t-a)$$ $$+ \mathscr{U}(t-2a)$$ 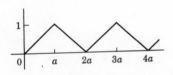	$$f_p(s) = \frac{1}{s}(1 - e^{-as})^2$$ $$f(s) = \frac{1}{s}\tanh\frac{as}{2}$$	3.5
Triangular-wave function $$F_p(t) = \frac{1}{a}[\mathscr{U}(t)t - 2\mathscr{U}(t-a)(t-a)$$ $$+ \mathscr{U}(t-2a)(t-2a)]$$	$$f_p(s) = \frac{(1 - e^{-as})^2}{as^2}$$ $$f(s) = \frac{1}{as^2}\tanh\frac{as}{2}$$	3.5
Half-wave rectification of sine wave $$F_p(t) = \mathscr{U}(t)\sin kt$$ $$+ \mathscr{U}\left(t - \frac{\pi}{k}\right)\sin k\left(t - \frac{\pi}{k}\right)$$	$$f_p(s) = \frac{k}{s^2 + k^2}\left(1 + e^{-\frac{\pi s}{k}}\right)$$ $$f(s) = \frac{k}{s^2 + k^2}\frac{1}{1 - e^{-\frac{\pi s}{k}}}$$	3.5

TABLE OF TRANSFORMS

F(t)	f(s)	§
Full-wave rectification of sine wave $$F_p(t) = \mathcal{U}(t)\sin kt$$ $$+ \mathcal{U}\left(t - \frac{\pi}{k}\right)\sin k\left(t - \frac{\pi}{k}\right)$$ $$F(t) = |\sin kt|$$	$$f_p(s) = \frac{k}{s^2 + k^2}\left(1 + e^{-\frac{\pi s}{k}}\right)$$ $$f(s) = \frac{k}{s^2 + k^2}\coth\frac{\pi s}{2k}$$	3.5
$$\mathcal{I}(t - t_0, \varepsilon) = \frac{1}{\varepsilon}\,[\mathcal{U}(t - t_0)$$ $$- \mathcal{U}(t - \overline{t_0 + \varepsilon})]$$	$$\frac{1 - e^{-s\varepsilon}}{s\varepsilon}\,e^{-st_0}$$	3.6
$\mathcal{I}(t - t_0)$	e^{-st_0}	3.6
$\mathcal{D}(t - t_0)$	se^{-st_0}	3.6
$\ln t$	$$\frac{\Gamma'(1)}{s} - \frac{\ln s}{s},$$ $$(\Gamma'(1) \doteq -.5772)$$	6.2
$t \ln t$	$$\frac{\Gamma'(2) - \ln s}{s^2}$$	6.2

F(t)	f(s)	§
$\dfrac{e^t}{\sqrt{\pi}} \displaystyle\int_0^t \dfrac{e^{-\tau}}{\sqrt{\tau}}\, d\tau$	$\dfrac{1}{\sqrt{s(s-1)}}$	6.3
$1 - \operatorname{erf} \dfrac{k}{2\sqrt{t}}$	$\dfrac{1}{s}\, e^{-k\sqrt{s}}, \quad (k > 0)$	6.3
$\dfrac{e^{-\frac{k^2}{4t}}}{t^{3/2}}$	$\dfrac{2\sqrt{\pi}}{k}\, e^{-k\sqrt{s}}, \quad (k > 0)$	6.3

Appendix III

Glossary of Terms from the Calculus

Absolute Convergence of a Series of Functions. A convergent series of functions $\sum\limits_{i=1}^{\infty} F_i(t)$ is said to be absolutely convergent at $t = c$ if and only if $\sum\limits_{i=1}^{\infty} |F_i(t)|$ converges at $t = c$.

Absolute Convergence of an Improper Integral. A convergent improper integral $\int_a^b F(s, t)\, dt$ is said to be absolutely convergent at $s = c$ if and only if $\int_a^b |F(s, t)|\, dt$ converges for $s = c$.

Beta Function. The improper integral $B(x, y) = \int_0^1 t^{x-1}(1 - t)^{y-1}\, dt$, $(0 < x,\ 0 < y)$, is called the beta function of x and y.

Bounded Function. $F(t)$ is bounded on the interval $a \le t \le b$ if and only if there exists a constant M such that $|F(t)| \le M$ for all t on the interval.

Continuity. $F(t)$ is continuous at $t = c$ if and only if $F(c)$ is a finite number and equals $\lim\limits_{t \to c} F(t)$. In other words, $F(t)$ is continuous at $t = c$ if and only if $F(c)$ is a finite number and corresponding to an arbitrary positive number ε there exists a $\delta > 0$ depending on ε such that $|F(c) - F(t)| < \varepsilon$ for all t such that $|t - c| < \delta$.

Convergence of a Series of Functions. An infinite series of functions $\sum\limits_{i=1}^{\infty} F_i(t)$ is convergent at $t = c$ if corresponding to an arbitrary positive number ε there exists an integer N depending on ε such that $\left| \sum\limits_{i=m+1}^{n} F_i(c) \right| < \varepsilon$ for all $n > m > N$. Hence, given an $\varepsilon > 0$ there exists an integer N depending on ε such that $\left| \sum\limits_{i=n+1}^{\infty} F_i(c) \right| < \varepsilon$ for all $n > N$, when the series converges at $t = c$.

Convergence of an Improper Integral. Two cases arise (see Improper Integral):

(a) The integral is improper because the range of integration is infinite, for instance $a = 0$ and $b = \infty$. In this case, let $\int_0^T F(c, t)\, dt$ exist for all finite $T > 0$, and some constant c. Then the improper integral $\int_0^\infty F(s, t)\, dt$ is convergent for $s = c$ if corresponding to an arbitrary positive number ε there exists a constant N depending on ε such that $\left| \int_m^n F(c, t)\, dt \right| < \varepsilon$ for all $n > m > N$, or briefly, $\lim\limits_{n,m \to \infty} \int_m^n F(c, t)\, dt = 0$. Hence, given an $\varepsilon > 0$ there exists a constant N depending on ε such that $\left| \int_n^\infty F(c, t)\, dt \right| < \varepsilon$ for all $n > N$, or briefly, $\lim\limits_{n \to \infty} \int_n^\infty F(c, t)\, dt = 0$, when the integral converges.

(b) The integral $\int_a^b F(s, t)\, dt$ is improper because the function $F(c, t)$ fails to have a right-hand or left-hand limit for some $t = d$, where $a \le d \le b$. For instance, if $a < d < b$, then briefly, $\int_a^b F(c, t)\, dt = \lim\limits_{\varepsilon_1 \to 0^+} \int_a^{d-\varepsilon_1} F(c, t)\, dt + \lim\limits_{\varepsilon_2 \to 0^+} \int_{d+\varepsilon_2}^b F(c, t)\, dt$, provided d is the only value of t at which the integrand fails to have a limit in the interval of integration.

Exponential Order. A function $F(t)$ is said to be of exponential order e^{at} if corresponding to the constant a there exists a pair of positive constants t_0 and M such that for all t at which $F(t)$ is defined and $t > t_0$, $\left| e^{-at} F(t) \right| \le M$.

Finite Discontinuity. If $F(t)$ is discontinuous at $t = c$ and if $F(c^-)$ and $F(c^+)$ are finite, then $F(t)$ is said to have a finite discontinuity at $t = c$.

Gamma Function. The improper integral

$$\Gamma(x) = \int_0^\infty e^{-t} t^{x-1}\, dt, \qquad (0 < x < \infty),$$

is called the gamma function of x.

Improper Integral. An integral $\int_a^b F(x)\, dx$ is improper in the following cases:

(a) a or b is infinite,

(b) $F(x)$ fails to have a right-hand or left-hand limit somewhere in the interval $a \le x \le b$.

Indeterminate Forms. If (a) $f(x) \to 0$ and $g(x) \to 0$ as $x \to c^+$, or (b) $f(x) \to \infty$ and $g(x) \to \infty$ as $x \to c^+$, then $\dfrac{f(c^+)}{g(c^+)} \left(= \dfrac{0}{0} \text{ or } \dfrac{\infty}{\infty} \right)$ is an example of what is usually called an indeterminate form. Its evaluation, when it exists, can often be made by application of L'Hospital's Rule. (An analogous statement applies when $x \to c^-$.)

Infinite Discontinuity of Order $t^{-\alpha}$. Suppose $F(t)$ is unbounded as $t \to 0$. If for some α, $(0 < \alpha < 1)$, the function $F(t)$ has the property that there exist positive constants M and t_0 such that $|t^\alpha F(t)| \le M$ whenever $0 < t < t_0$, then $F(t)$ is said to have an infinite discontinuity of order $t^{-\alpha}$ at $t = 0$.

Jump. If $F(c^+)$ and $F(c^-)$ are finite, then $F(c^+) - F(c^-)$ is called the jump of $F(t)$ at $t = c$.

Left-hand [Right-hand] Limit. If $F(t)$ is defined in an interval $a \le t < c$ $[c < t \le b]$, and $\lim\limits_{\substack{t \to c \\ t < c}} F(t)$ $[\lim\limits_{\substack{t \to c \\ t > c}} F(t)]$ is finite, then this limit is the left-hand limit [right-hand limit], denoted by $F(c^-)$ $[F(c^+)]$, of $F(t)$ at c.

L'Hospital's Rule. If $\lim\limits_{x \to c} \dfrac{f(x)}{g(x)}$ is of the form 0/0 or ∞/∞, and if $\lim\limits_{x \to c} \dfrac{f'(x)}{g'(x)}$ exists, then $\lim\limits_{x \to c} \dfrac{f(x)}{g(x)} = \lim\limits_{x \to c} \dfrac{f'(x)}{g'(x)}$. This holds whether c is finite or infinite, and applies to right-hand or left-hand limits as well. For the specific conditions $f(x)$ and $g(x)$ must satisfy, see the advanced calculus texts listed in the bibliography.

Monotonic Function. $F(t)$ is called a monotonic non-decreasing function of t if $F(t)$ does not decrease as t increases; that is, if $F(t_1) \le F(t_2)$ whenever $t_1 < t_2$. A similar definition applies to monotonic non-increasing functions.

Sectional Continuity. A function $F(t)$ is said to be sectionally continuous for $t \ge 0$ if it is continuous except for at most a finite number of finite discontinuities in the interval $0 \le t \le b$ for all $b > 0$.

Uniform Continuity. $F(t)$ is uniformly continuous on the finite interval $a \le t \le b$ if and only if corresponding to an arbitrary positive number ε there exists a $\delta > 0$ depending on ε but independent of t' and t'' and such that $|F(t') - F(t'')| < \varepsilon$, where t', t'' are any two values of t in the interval $a \le t \le b$ such that $|t' - t''| < \delta$.

Uniform Convergence of a Series of Functions. A convergent series of functions $\sum\limits_{i=1}^{\infty} F_i(t)$ is said to converge uniformly on a finite interval $a \le t \le b$ if and only if corresponding to an arbitrary positive number ε there exists an integer N depending on ε but independent of t such that $\left| \sum\limits_{i=m+1}^{n} F_i(t) \right| < \varepsilon$ for all t in the interval and for all $n > m > N$. Hence, given $\varepsilon > 0$ there exists an integer N depending on ε but independent of t such that $\left| \sum\limits_{i=n}^{\infty} F_i(t) \right| < \varepsilon$ for all t in the interval and for all $n > N$, when the series is uniformly convergent.

Uniform Convergence of an Improper Integral. A convergent improper integral $\int_0^{\infty} F(s, t)\, dt$ is said to converge uniformly on a finite interval $A \leq s \leq B$ if and only if corresponding to an arbitrary positive number ε there exists a constant N depending on ε but independent of s such that $\left| \int_m^n F(s, t)\, dt \right| < \varepsilon$ for all s in the interval and all $n > m > N$. Hence, given $\varepsilon > 0$ there exists a constant N such that $\left| \int_n^{\infty} F(s, t)\, dt \right| < \varepsilon$ for all s in the interval and all $n > N$, when the integral is uniformly convergent. An analogous definition applies to an improper integral with finite limits a and b. For instance, if $a = d$ (see Convergence of an Improper Integral) then $\int_a^b F(s, t)\, dt$ is said to converge uniformly on the interval $A \leq s \leq B$ if and only if corresponding to an arbitrary positive number ε there exists a positive constant δ depending on ε but independent of s such that $\left| \int_a^{a+\delta} F(s, t) \right| < \varepsilon$ for all s in the interval.

Appendix IV

Definitions and Laws
for Electrical Circuits

The *current* (electric) I is the time rate of flow of the charge Q, that is, $I = \dfrac{dQ}{dt}$.

A *cycle* is the chronologically ordered collection of values that a periodic function of time assumes in the course of its least period.

The *frequency* of a periodic function is the number of *cycles per second*. Unless otherwise stated the term *cycles* means "cycles per second".

The *potential difference* (or voltage drop) across a *resistance* R through which a current I is flowing is given by $V = IR$.

The potential difference V across a *condenser* of *capacitance* C on which there is a charge Q is given by

$$V = \frac{Q}{C} = \frac{1}{C}\int I\, dt.$$

ELECTRICAL SYMBOLS

Resistance   Capacitance   Inductance

Variable voltage   Constant voltage

The potential difference V across a *coil* of *inductance* L through which there is flowing a current I changing at the rate $\dfrac{dI}{dt}$ is given by

$$V = L\frac{dI}{dt}.$$

158

A *voltage source* may be a generator if the voltage is variable or a battery or D.C. generator if the voltage is constant.

Any of the above elements or any group of elements connected in series (in linear sequence) is called a *branch*. Any simple closed path made up of one or more branches is called a *loop* of the circuit.

The terminals of the above elements are called *nodes*.

Kirchhoff's laws.

1. The algebraic sum of the voltage drops (the potential differences) across the elements of any loop is zero.

2. The algebraic sum of the currents flowing into any node in an electrical network is zero.

Answers

CHAPTER 1

Exercises 1, page 6

1. (a) $\dfrac{3}{s} + \dfrac{2}{s^2}$ (b) $\dfrac{2}{s^3}$ (c) $\dfrac{6}{s+2}$ (d) $\dfrac{15}{s^2-9}$ (e) $\dfrac{4}{s(s^2+4)}$

2. (b) $\dfrac{5}{s} - \dfrac{1}{s^2} + \dfrac{4}{s^3} + \dfrac{6}{s^4}$ **6.** (c) i. $\dfrac{6}{s^2+2s+5}$ ii. $\dfrac{4s-8}{s^2-4s+13}$

Exercises 2, page 9

1. (a) $\dfrac{1}{(s-3)^2}$ (b) $\dfrac{s}{(s+1)^2}$ (c) $\dfrac{6}{(s-5)^4}$

6. (a) $3e^{-t}\sin 2t$ (b) $2e^{-3t}$ (c) $8e^{-2t}\cosh 3t$ (d) $\dfrac{1}{36}\sin\dfrac{4}{9}t$

Exercises 4, page 20

1. $1 - e^{-t}$ **2.** $\frac{1}{2}[e^{-t} - \cos t + \sin t]$

3. $\frac{1}{2}t^2 e^{-t}$ **4.** $\frac{1}{2}[e^t - \cos t + \sin t]$

5. $e^{-t} - (t+1)e^{-2t}$ **6.** $\frac{1}{2} + \frac{1}{2}e^{2t} - e^t$

7. $\frac{1}{2} + \frac{1}{2}e^{2t} - e^t$ **8.** $e^{-3t} - e^{-7t}$

9. $X(t) = e^t + \frac{3}{2}te^t + \frac{1}{2}te^{-t}$

     $Y(t) = -5e^t - 3te^t + e^{-t} - te^{-t}$

10. $X(t) = -7 + 2t + e^{(3/2)t}\left[8\cosh\dfrac{\sqrt{13}}{2}t - \dfrac{30}{\sqrt{13}}\sinh\dfrac{\sqrt{13}}{2}t\right]$

     $Y(t) = 25 - 4t - e^{(3/2)t}\left[24\cosh\dfrac{\sqrt{13}}{2}t - \dfrac{90}{\sqrt{13}}\sinh\dfrac{\sqrt{13}}{2}t\right]$

     $Z(t) = -3 + e^{(3/2)t}\left[3\cosh\dfrac{\sqrt{13}}{2}t - \dfrac{7}{\sqrt{13}}\sinh\dfrac{\sqrt{13}}{2}t\right]$

11. $X(t) = e^{-2t} + 2te^{-2t}$

     $Y(t) = -\frac{1}{3}e^{-2t} - \frac{2}{3}te^{-2t}$

     $Z(t) = -\frac{2}{3}e^{-2t} - \frac{4}{3}te^{-2t}$

Exercises 5, page 31

1. $-2e^t + e^{2t} + 2e^{3t}$

2. $e^t - e^{-t} - t$

3. $8 + 5t + t^2 - 8e^t + 3te^t$

4. $1 - \cos kt$

5. $\sinh kt - \sin kt$

6. $\cosh kt - \cos kt$

7. $\sinh kt + \sin kt$

8. $\cosh kt + \cos kt$

9. $\frac{1}{6}e^{-2t} + \frac{1}{2}te^{-t} - \frac{1}{5}\cos t - \frac{1}{10}\sin t$

10. $\dfrac{1}{a^2 - b^2}(\cos bt - \cos at)$

11. $\frac{3}{26}\cos 3t - \frac{1}{13}\sin 3t - \frac{3}{26}e^t \cos 2t + \frac{9}{52}e^t \sin 2t$

12. $140[-\frac{4}{3}\sin 3t + \frac{7}{6}\sin 2t + \frac{5}{8}\sin 4t]$ 13. $6\cos 3t + \frac{7}{3}\cos 2t - \frac{25}{3}\cos 4t$

CHAPTER 2

Exercises 1, page 38

1. (a) $\dfrac{e^{-s}}{s^2}(s + 1)$ (b) $\dfrac{s}{s^2 + 1}(e^{-\pi s} + 1) + \dfrac{e^{-\pi s}}{s}$

3. (a) Continuous, exponential order, class T
   (b) Exponential order
   (c) Exponential order
   (d) Continuous, exponential order, class T
   (e) Sectionally continuous, exponential order, class T
   (f) Continuous, exponential order, class T
   (g) Sectionally continuous, exponential order, class T
   (h) Class T

Exercises 2, page 42

1. $\dfrac{-se^{-\pi s}}{s^2 + 1}$ 2. $\dfrac{-(1 + e^{-\pi s})}{s^2 + 1}$

Exercises 3, page 49

1. (a) $\dfrac{t^3}{6}$ (b) $\frac{1}{2}(e^t - e^{-t})$ (c) $\dfrac{t^{n+1}}{n + 1}$

2. (a) t (b) $1 - e^{-t}$

   (c) $\dfrac{e^{at} - e^{-bt}}{a - b}$, $a \neq b$; te^{at}, $a = b$

   (d) $\frac{1}{2}(-e^{-t} + \sin t + \cos t)$ (e) $\dfrac{1}{2}\left(t\cos kt + \dfrac{1}{k}\sin kt\right)$

   (f) $\dfrac{e^{at}}{4a^2 + k^2}(2a\sin kt - k\cos kt + ke^{-2at})$

3. (a) $-\dfrac{1}{k^2}(1 - \cosh kt)$ (b) $\dfrac{1}{k^3}(kt - \sin kt)$

Exercises 4, page 51

1. e^{at}

3. $\sin at$

2. $\cos t + \sin t$

4. $\dfrac{k^2 - 1}{k^2} \cos kt + \dfrac{1}{k^2}$

Exercises 5, page 56

1. $\dfrac{t}{2} \sin t$

5. $J_0(it)$

3. (a) $\dfrac{t}{2} + Ce^{-t}$ (b) $At^2 e^t$ (c) $A(t + e^{-t} - 1)$

Exercises 7, page 61

2. (a) 0, 0   (c) 0, 8

   (b) 0, 0   (d) not applicable, 0.

3. (a) 0   (b) 0   (c) 2

CHAPTER 3

Exercises 1, page 65

1. $\mathcal{U}(t) - \mathcal{U}(t-1) + [\mathcal{U}(t-1) - \mathcal{U}(t-2)](4t - t^2) + \mathcal{U}(t-2)$

2. $\mathcal{U}\left(t - \dfrac{\pi}{2}\right) \sin t$

3. $\mathcal{U}(t) - \mathcal{U}(t-1) + \mathcal{U}(t-1)e^{t-1}$

4. $[\mathcal{U}(t) - \mathcal{U}(t-1)]t^2 - [\mathcal{U}(t-1) - \mathcal{U}(t-3)](t^2 - 4t + 2)$
$$+ [\mathcal{U}(t-3) - \mathcal{U}(t-4)](t-4)^2$$

5. $\dfrac{1}{1 + s^2}(e^{-3\pi s} - e^{-\pi s})$

6. $e^{-s}\left(-\dfrac{1}{s} - \dfrac{e}{1-s} + \dfrac{2e^{-s}}{s}\right) + \dfrac{1}{s} + \dfrac{e^{-2s+2}}{1-s}$

7. $\dfrac{1}{s} + \dfrac{1}{s^2}(e^{-3s} - e^{-s})$

8. $\dfrac{5}{s}e^{-3s} + \dfrac{3e^{-s}}{s} + \dfrac{6e^{-3s}}{s^2} - \dfrac{2e^{-s}}{s^2} + \dfrac{2e^{-3s}}{s^3} - \dfrac{2e^{-s}}{s^3}$

Exercises 2, page 69

1. $e^{-s}\left[\dfrac{6}{s^4} + \dfrac{1}{s^2} + \dfrac{6}{s}\right]$

2. (a) $e^{-2\pi s}\dfrac{s}{s^2 + 1}$ (b) $-e^{-\pi s}\dfrac{1}{s^2 + 1}$

3. $\mathcal{U}(t)t - \mathcal{U}(t-1)(t-1)$

4. $\mathcal{U}(t)t - \mathcal{U}(t-1)2(t-1) + \mathcal{U}(t-2)(t-2)$

5. $\mathcal{U}(t)t - \mathcal{U}(t-1)4(t-1) + \mathcal{U}(t-2)6(t-2) - \mathcal{U}(t-3)4t(t-3)$
$$+ \mathcal{U}(t-4)(t-4)$$

7. (a) $\mathcal{U}(t-a)\sin(t-a)$

   (b) $\mathcal{U}(t-2)e^{t-2}$

   (c) $\mathcal{U}(t-3)\cosh(t-3)$

Exercises 3, page 73

1. Fig. 14: $\dfrac{e^{-s}}{s^2} - \dfrac{e^{-2s}(s+1)}{s^2}$

   Fig. 15: $\dfrac{1}{as^2}(1 - e^{-as})^2$

2. Fig. 16: $\dfrac{1}{2}\left[\dfrac{2}{s} - \dfrac{1}{s^2} + \dfrac{e^{-s}}{s^2} - \dfrac{e^{-2s}}{s}\right]$

   Fig. 17: $\dfrac{1}{s^2}(1 - e^{-s} - e^{-2s} + e^{-3s})$

   Fig. 18: $\dfrac{1}{s}(e^{-s} + e^{-3s}) - \dfrac{1}{s^2}(e^{-s} - e^{-3s})$

3. $\dfrac{1 - e^{-2\pi s} - 2e^{-4\pi s}}{s^2 + 1}$

4. (a) $\dfrac{(1 - e^{-as})^2}{s^2}$ (b) 0 (c) $\dfrac{e^{-4as}}{s^2}(1 - e^{-as})^2$

5. $\mathcal{U}(t) - 2\mathcal{U}(t-a) + \mathcal{U}(t-2a)$

6. $\mathcal{U}(t) - \mathcal{U}(t-1)(t-1) - \mathcal{U}(t-3)(t-3) + \mathcal{U}(t-5)(t-5)$
$$+ \mathcal{U}(t-7)(t-7) - \mathcal{U}(t-8)(t-8),$$
$\dfrac{1}{s^2}(1 - e^{-s} - e^{-3s} + e^{-5s} + e^{-7s} - e^{-8s})$

Exercises 4, page 76

1. (a) $\dfrac{1}{s^2}\dfrac{(1 - e^{-s})(1 - e^{-2s})}{1 - e^{-3s}}$ (b) $\dfrac{1}{s^2}\dfrac{1 - e^{-s}}{1 + e^{-2s}}$

   (c) $\dfrac{(s+1)e^{-3s} + (s-1)e^{-s}}{s^2(1 - e^{-3s})}$

   (d) $\dfrac{1}{s^2(1 - e^{-8s})}(1 - e^{-s} - e^{-3s} + e^{-5s} + e^{-7s} - e^{-8s})$

2. $\dfrac{1}{s(1 + e^{-as})}$

3. $\left(\dfrac{\pi}{s^2 + \pi^2}\right)\left(\dfrac{1}{1 - e^{-s}}\right)$

4. (a) $\dfrac{(s - 2)e^{-s} - e^{-2s}(s + 2)}{s^3}$

    (b) $\dfrac{e^{-s}}{s^2(1 + e^{-s})} - 2\,\dfrac{e^{-s}}{s^3(1 - e^{-s})}$

5. $F_p(t) = \mathscr{U}(t) + \mathscr{U}(t - 1) + \mathscr{U}(t - 2) - \mathscr{U}(t - 3) - \mathscr{U}(t - 4) - \mathscr{U}(t - 5),$

    $f(s) = \dfrac{1}{(1 - e^{-7s})}\,f_p(s)$

6. $f_p(s) = \dfrac{1}{s^3}(1 - e^{-2s})(1 - e^{-s})^2$

    $f(s) = \dfrac{f_p(s)}{1 - e^{-4s}} = \dfrac{1}{2s^3}\dfrac{(1 - e^{-s})^2}{1 + e^{-2s}}$

7. $\dfrac{1}{s^2}(1 - e^{-2s})(1 - e^{-s})^2$

8. (a) $\mathscr{U}(t)(t - 1) + \mathscr{U}(t - 1)(t - 1),\qquad (T = 2)$

    (b) $\mathscr{U}(t) + \mathscr{U}(t - \tfrac{1}{2}) - 2\mathscr{U}(t - 1),\qquad (T = 3)$

        $= 1,\quad 0 \le t < \tfrac{1}{2},$

           $2,\quad \tfrac{1}{2} \le t < 1,$

           $0,\quad 1 \le t < 3.$

Exercises 5, page 81

2. (a) $\mathscr{I}(t) - ae^{-at}$ (b) $\mathscr{I}(t) - \sin t$

    (c) $\mathscr{I}(t) - \tfrac{1}{3}\left[e^{-t} - e^{\frac{t}{2}}\left(\cos\dfrac{\sqrt{3}}{2}t - \sqrt{3}\sin\dfrac{\sqrt{3}}{2}t\right)\right]$

3. (a) $\dfrac{e^{-s}}{1 - e^{-s}}\left(= \sum_{n=1}^{\infty} e^{-sn}\right)$ (b) $\dfrac{1}{e^s + 1}$

Exercises 6, page 87

1. (a) $Y_1 = \tfrac{1}{6} - \tfrac{1}{2}e^{-2t} + \tfrac{1}{3}e^{-3t}$

      $Y_2 = e^{-2t} - e^{-3t}$

    (b) $Y_1 = \tfrac{1}{2}[1 + e^t(\sin t - \cos t)]$

      $Y_2 = e^t \sin t$

Exercises 7, page 89

1. $X_0(1 - \gamma^2 Y_1(t))$

    where $Y_1(t) = \dfrac{1}{a^2 + b^2}\left[1 - \dfrac{e^{-at}}{b}(a \sin bt + b \cos bt)\right]$

2. $\frac{1}{25}(1 - \frac{3}{4}e^{-3t}\sin 4t - e^{-3t}\cos 4t)$

4. $e^{-3t}(\frac{19}{25}\cos 4t + \frac{57}{100}\sin 4t) + \frac{6}{25}$

5. $\frac{1}{65} + e^{-t}(\frac{2}{13}\sin 13t + \frac{167}{169}\cos 13t)$

6. (a) $e^{-t}(\cos t + 11\sin t)$

    (b) $e^{-t}\left(\cos t + \dfrac{2e - \cos 1}{\sin 1}\sin t\right)$

    (c) $-\frac{1}{2}e^{\frac{\pi}{2}}e^{-t}(\cos t + \sin t)$

7. $\dfrac{F_0}{2\gamma^2}(\sin \gamma t - \gamma t\cos \gamma t)$ **8.** $\frac{1}{4}\mathcal{U}(t - 1)e^{-3(t-1)}\sin 4(t - 1)$

CHAPTER 4

Exercises 1, page 97

1. $\dfrac{F_0}{2a\omega}(\sin \omega t - i\cos \omega t)$

2. $Q_0 e^{-\frac{t}{RC}} + F_0 C[\mathcal{U}(t - t_1) - \mathcal{U}(t - t_2) - \mathcal{U}(t - t_1)e^{-\frac{t - t_1}{RC}}$
$$+ \mathcal{U}(t - t_2)e^{-\frac{t - t_2}{RC}}]$$

3. $E_0 C\left[1 - \cos\dfrac{t}{\sqrt{LC}} - \mathcal{U}(t - t_0)\left(1 - \cos\dfrac{t - t_0}{\sqrt{LC}}\right.\right.$
$$\left.\left. + \frac{t_0}{\sqrt{LC}}\sin\frac{t - t_0}{\sqrt{LC}}\right)\right]$$

4. $I(t) = \dfrac{E_0\omega}{L(\omega^2 - \gamma^2)}(\cos \gamma t - \cos \omega t)$

    $Q(t) = \dfrac{E_0}{2L\omega^2}(\sin \omega t - 2\omega t\cos \omega t)$

5. $\dfrac{E_1\cos(\omega_1 t - \theta_1)}{\sqrt{4a^2\omega_1^2 + (\gamma^2 - \omega_1^2)^2}} + \dfrac{E_2\cos(\omega_2 t - \theta_2)}{\sqrt{4a^2\omega_2^2 + (\gamma^2 - \omega_2^2)^2}},$

    $\tan \theta_i = \dfrac{2a\omega_i}{\gamma^2 - \omega_i^2}, \ (i = 1, 2), \qquad a = \dfrac{R}{2L}, \qquad \gamma^2 = \dfrac{1}{LC}$

6. $(-1)^n - (2n + 1)\cos\frac{\pi}{T}t, \qquad (nT \le t < (n + 1)T), \qquad (n = 0, 1, 2, \ldots)$

7. $\dfrac{E_0}{R(\omega^2 + a^4)}\Big\{a^2\cos \omega t + \omega\sin \omega t - a^2 e^{-a^2 t}$

$$+ 2\sum_{n=1}^{\infty}\mathcal{U}\left(t - \frac{n\pi}{\omega}\right)\left[a^2\cos \omega\left(t - \frac{n\pi}{\omega}\right) + \omega\sin \omega\left(t - \frac{n\pi}{\omega}\right)\right.$$

$$\left. - a^2 e^{-a^2\left(t - \frac{n\pi}{\omega}\right)}\right]\Big\}, \left(a^2 = \frac{1}{RC}\right).$$

8. $\dfrac{E_0}{R(a^4 + b^2)} \displaystyle\sum_{n=0}^{\infty} \mathscr{U}\left(t - \dfrac{2n\pi}{b}\right)\left[a^4 e^{-a^2\left(t - \frac{2n\pi}{b}\right)} + b^2 \cos b\left(t - \dfrac{2n\pi}{b}\right)\right.$

$$\left. - a^2 b \sin b\left(t - \dfrac{2n\pi}{b}\right)\right]$$

$$+ \dfrac{E_0 b}{R(a^4 + b^2)} \sum_{n=0}^{\infty} \mathscr{U}\left(t - \dfrac{4n+1}{b}\pi\right)\left[-a^2 e^{-a^2\left(t - \frac{4n+1}{b}\pi\right)}\right.$$

$$\left. + a^2 \cos b\left(t - \dfrac{4n+1}{b}\pi\right) + b \sin b\left(t - \dfrac{4n+1}{b}\pi\right)\right]$$

9. $\dfrac{10aA}{m}$

Exercises 2, page 101

1. $k_2 = 3, \quad m_2 = \tfrac{3}{4}$

2. $x_1(s) = \dfrac{k_1\omega(m_2 s^2 + k_2)}{(s^2 + \omega^2)[m_1 m_2 s^4 + (m_1 k_2 + m_2 k_1 + m_2 k_2)s^2 + k_1 k_2]}$

$x_2(s) = \dfrac{k_1\omega(cs + k_2)}{(s^2 + \omega^2)[m_1 m_2 s^4 + (m_1 k_2 + m_1 k_1 + m_2 k_2)s^2 + k_1 k_2]}$

Exercises 3, page 104

1. For $m = 1$, $r = c > 0$, $\quad x(s) = \dfrac{F_0}{(s^2 + k)(s + c)}$, stable

2. $\dfrac{F_0}{ms^3 + (c + ch)s^2 + (cr + k + kh)s + kr}$

3. For $F(t) = F_0\mathscr{U}(t)$, $\quad x(s) = \dfrac{F_0}{ms^3 + (c + kr)s^2 + (k + kh)s}$, stable

4. $\dfrac{bX_0[(a - h)s - r]}{s[ABs^3 + (-aB + bB + bA)s^2 - (ab + bh)s - br]}$,

$\displaystyle\lim_{t\to\infty} X(t) = X_0$

Exercises 4, page 109

1. $\dfrac{2}{9}Pa^2 x + \dfrac{w_0 a^3}{48} - \dfrac{w_0 a^4}{384} - \dfrac{4Pa^3}{21}$

2. $-AY''(0) = -\dfrac{4}{27}Pa + \dfrac{1}{4}M - \dfrac{1}{108}w_0 a^2$, $\quad -AY'''(0) = \dfrac{20}{27}\left(P + \dfrac{w_0 a}{24}\right)$,

$AY(t) = AY''(0)\dfrac{x^2}{2} + \dfrac{AY'''(0)x^3}{6} + \dfrac{1}{6}P\mathscr{U}\left(x - \dfrac{a}{3}\right)\left(x - \dfrac{a}{3}\right)^3$

$\qquad + \dfrac{1}{2}M\mathscr{U}\left(x - \dfrac{a}{2}\right)\left(x - \dfrac{a}{2}\right)^2 + \dfrac{w_0}{24}\left[\mathscr{U}\left(x - \dfrac{2a}{3}\right)\left(x - \dfrac{2a}{3}\right)^4\right.$

$$\left. - \mathscr{U}(x - a)(x - a)^4\right]$$

3. $\dfrac{5}{16}P + \dfrac{7}{4}w_0 a$

CHAPTER 5

Exercises 2, page 116

1. $2\mathscr{U}\left(t - \dfrac{x}{a}\right) \sin 3\left(t - \dfrac{x}{a}\right)$

2. $\dfrac{1}{\pi} \sin \pi x \sin \pi t.$

3. $\dfrac{2}{s^3} \dfrac{\cosh s(x - \frac{1}{2})}{\cosh \dfrac{s}{2}} + \dfrac{1}{s}(x - x^2) - \dfrac{2}{s^3}$

4. $\dfrac{g}{s^3}\left[\dfrac{\cosh \dfrac{s(L - 2x)}{2a}}{\cosh \dfrac{sL}{2a}} - 1\right] + \dfrac{Cs}{s^2 + \dfrac{a^2\pi^2}{L^2}} \sin \dfrac{\pi x}{L}$

5. $\dfrac{g}{2}\left(\mathscr{U}\left(t - \dfrac{x}{a}\right)\left(t - \dfrac{x}{a}\right)^2 - t^2\right)$

Exercises 3, page 121

1. $a \displaystyle\sum_{k=0}^{\infty} (-1)^k\left[\left(t - \dfrac{(2k + 1)L - x}{a}\right)\mathscr{U}\left(t - \dfrac{(2k + 1)L - x}{a}\right)\right.$

$\left. - \left(t - \dfrac{(2k + 1)L + x}{a}\right)\mathscr{U}\left(t - \dfrac{(2k + 1)L + x}{a}\right)\right]$

$-a \displaystyle\sum_{k=0}^{\infty} (-1)^k\left[\left(t - t_0 - \dfrac{(2k + 1)L - x}{a}\right)\mathscr{U}\left(t - t_0 - \dfrac{(2k + 1)L - x}{a}\right)\right.$

$\left. - \left(t - t_0 - \dfrac{(2k + 1)L + x}{a}\right)\mathscr{U}\left(t - t_0 - \dfrac{(2k + 1)L + x}{a}\right)\right]$

2. $\dfrac{L_0 - L}{L} x - \dfrac{L_0 - L}{L} a \displaystyle\sum_{k=0}^{\infty} (-1)^k\left[\left(t - \dfrac{(2k + 1)L - x}{a}\right)\right.$

$\mathscr{U}\left(t - \dfrac{(2k + 1)L - x}{a}\right) - \left(t - \dfrac{(2k + 1)L + x}{a}\right)\mathscr{U}\left(t - \dfrac{(2k + 1)L + x}{a}\right)\right]$

Exercises 4, page 124

1. (a) $U_1 + (U_0 - U_1)\left[1 - \operatorname{erf}\left(\dfrac{x}{2\sqrt{at}}\right)\right].$

(b) $U_1 x + U_0\left[1 - \operatorname{erf}\left(\dfrac{x}{2\sqrt{at}}\right)\right].$

(c) $U_0\left[t - \displaystyle\int_0^t \operatorname{erf}\left(\dfrac{x}{2\sqrt{a\tau}}\right) d\tau\right] + U_1 \operatorname{erf}\left(\dfrac{x}{2\sqrt{at}}\right).$

2. $A_1 - \dfrac{a(A_1 - A_2)}{1 + a} \operatorname{erfc}\left(\dfrac{-x}{2\sqrt{a_1 t}}\right)$, $(x < 0)$, $\operatorname{erfc}(y) = 1 - \operatorname{erf}(y)$

$A_2 + \dfrac{A_1 - A_2}{1 + a} \operatorname{erfc}\left(\dfrac{x}{2\sqrt{a_2 t}}\right)$, $(x > 0)$, $\left(a = \sqrt{\dfrac{a_2}{a_1}}\right)$.

Exercises 5, page 129

1. $U_0[1 - G(x, t)]$, where

$$G(x, t) = \sum_{k=0}^{\infty} (-1)^k \left[\operatorname{erfc}\left(\dfrac{(2k + 1)L - x}{2\sqrt{at}}\right) + \operatorname{erfc}\dfrac{(2k + 1)L + x}{2\sqrt{at}}\right)\right]$$

2. $F_0\left(t - \displaystyle\int_0^t G(x, \tau)\, d\tau\right)$, where $G(x, t)$ is given in 1

3. $[\mathscr{U}(t)t - \mathscr{U}(t - t_0)(t - t_0)](1 - \displaystyle\int_0^t G(x, \tau)\, d\tau)$,

where $G(x, t)$ is given in 1

4. $U_0 \displaystyle\sum_{k=0}^{\infty} \left[\operatorname{erfc}\dfrac{(2k + 1)L - x}{2\sqrt{at}} - \operatorname{erfc}\dfrac{(2k + 1)L + x}{2\sqrt{at}}\right.$

$\left. - \operatorname{erfc}\dfrac{2kL + x}{2\sqrt{at}} + \operatorname{erfc}\dfrac{2(k + 1)L - x}{2\sqrt{at}}\right]$

Exercises 6, page 133

1. $V_1 - (V_1 - V_0)\left[1 - \operatorname{erf}\left(\dfrac{x}{2}\sqrt{\dfrac{RC}{t}}\right)\right]$.

2. $V_1 + (V_0 - V_1)\displaystyle\sum_{k=0}^{\infty} \left[\operatorname{erfc}\left(\dfrac{2kL + x}{2}\sqrt{\dfrac{RC}{t}}\right)\right.$

$\left. - \operatorname{erfc}\left(\dfrac{2(k + 1)L - x}{2}\sqrt{\dfrac{RC}{t}}\right)\right]$

$- V_1 \displaystyle\sum_{k=0}^{\infty} \left[\operatorname{erfc}\left(\dfrac{(2k + 1)L - x}{2}\sqrt{\dfrac{RC}{t}}\right) - \operatorname{erfc}\left(\dfrac{(2k + 1)L + x}{2}\sqrt{\dfrac{RC}{t}}\right)\right]$

3. $V_0 \sin 3t * \displaystyle\sum_{k=0}^{\infty} \left[\dfrac{2kL + x}{2\sqrt{\pi t^3}} e^{-\frac{RC(2kL + x)^2}{4t}}\right.$

$\left. - \dfrac{2(k + 1)L - x}{2\sqrt{\pi t^3}} e^{-\frac{RC[2(k + 1)L - x]^2}{4t}}\right]$

4. $V_0 e^{-\frac{B}{A}t} \operatorname{erf}\left(\dfrac{x\sqrt{A}}{2\sqrt{t}}\right) + V_1[\mathscr{U}(t) - \mathscr{U}(t - t_0)] * \dfrac{x}{2}\sqrt{\dfrac{A}{\pi t^3}} e^{-\left(\frac{B}{A}t + \frac{Ax^2}{4t}\right)}$

5. $\mathcal{U}(t - x\sqrt{LC})F(t - x\sqrt{LC})$

6. (a) $\mathcal{U}(t - x\sqrt{LC})$

   (b) $\mathcal{U}(t - x\sqrt{LC})(t - x\sqrt{LC})$

   (c) $\mathcal{U}(t - x\sqrt{LC}) \sin \omega(t - x\sqrt{LC})$

CHAPTER 6

Exercises 1, page 136

3. (a) Yes, $\alpha = \frac{1}{2}$ (b) No, not of exponential order
   (c) Yes, $\alpha = \frac{3}{4}$ (d) Yes, $\alpha = \frac{1}{2}$

Exercises 2, page 138

4. $\dfrac{\Gamma'(2) - \ln s}{s^2}$

Index

171